ANIMALS IN FUR

New York, 1956

Animals in Fur

BY

CLARENCE J. HYLANDER

THE MACMILLAN COMPANY

49737

ACKNOWLEDGMENTS

The author acknowledges permission to reproduce the photographs in this book as follows: to the New York Zoological Society for photographs on endpapers, title page, facing page 1 and pages 22, 29, 53, 64, 84, 88, 96, 100, 102, 104, 106, 114, 119, 121, 125, 127, 152, 170, 186, 188, 189, 190.

Additional photographs and drawings are by the author. Drawings on pages 69, 93, 177, and 180 are adapted from drawings in *American Mammals* by W. J. Hamilton, Jr. (McGraw-Hill Book Company, 1939).

CONTENTS

Foreword   ix

Chapter 1 MEET THE MAMMALS   1

What is a mammal? What kinds of
mammals are native to the United
States? Where can mammals be found?
How do mammals vary in size?

Chapter 2 THE GNAWING MAMMALS   23

Tree squirrels and chipmunks. Ground
squirrels, marmots, and prairie dogs.
Pocket gophers. Mice and rats. Rabbits,
hares, and pikas.

Chapter 3 THE HOOFED MAMMALS   65

The deer family. The pronghorn family.
The cattle family.

Chapter 4 THE CARNIVORS   89

    The weasel family. The raccoon family.
    The bear family. The dog family. The
    cat family.

Chapter 5 THE SEA-GOING MAMMALS   131

    Seals and sea lions. Whales, porpoises
    and dolphins. The manatee.

Chapter 6 SOME UNUSUAL MAMMALS   153

    Opossum. Armadillo. Peccary. Moles.
    Bats.

Chapter 7 MAMMALS AT HOME   171

    The homes of mammals. Family life of
    mammals. How mammals spend the
    winter.

Afterword   198

Index   201

FOREWORD

ANIMALS IN FUR, as the title indicates, is the story of the fur-bearing animals; not all the furbearers, or mammals, that are known to man, but only those which live today in the United States. It is a series of animal biographies which attempt to bring out the personalities of the more interesting of our native mammals. It is not a field guide for the identification of mammals, although sufficient descriptive information is given for each species so that it can be recognized when you see it. There are a number of excellent and recent field guides already published, to which reference is made in the final chapter on "Mammal Books for a Nature Library."

Like the preceding books in "The Young Naturalist Series" (SEA AND SHORE, TREES AND TRAILS, ANIMALS IN ARMOR), this is an introduction to one of the biological sciences: mammalogy. Nature study is too often thought of merely as an interesting hobby. It is also an open door into the fascinating world of scientific research. By piecing together the observations of hundreds of field biologists, or naturalists, science is able to discover many ways in which we can live harmoniously and profitably with our native wild life. In ANIMALS IN FUR I have tried to bring to you some of the revealing facts about nature that mammalogists have painstakingly accumulated.

Fortunately for us the United States provides an unusually rich variety of environments for animals to live in, ranging from subarctic in our high mountains and northern states to subtropical in the Southwest and Florida. The special kind of environment in which a particular kind of animal or plant lives is known as its habitat. Mammals have shown an adventurous and enterprising disposition to colonize every conceivable habitat in this wide range. One of the most rewarding aspects of observing any group of animals is the amazing story one learns of how each species of the group has adapted itself for life in a particular habitat. Each habitat makes an indelible imprint upon the body and activities of its inhabitants. The result is such diversity of animals as the burrowing gophers, the leaping jack rabbits, the climbing squirrels, the fleet-footed deer, the powerful cougars, the flying bats, and the sea-going whales!

The central theme of the story of ANIMALS IN FUR is this adaptation of each kind of mammal to the living conditions of air, land, and water. As this story unfolds we will discover that in each animal various body structures and skills have developed, enabling the individual to solve the vital problems of food-getting and locomotion. Eating is associated with changes in a mammal's teeth to meet varied demands: those of a vegetarian, or herbivorous, diet, as in the deer and cattle families; of a meat-eating, or carnivorous, diet, as in the dog and cat families; of a less specialized, or omnivorous, diet as in some rodents and carnivors. This modification of the teeth is paralleled by changes in the mammal limb so that the animal can get around easily by the type of locomotion necessary in securing food of various types in different habitats. Hoofs, claws, flippers, and wings are Nature's answer to the requirements for locomotion on the ground, in the trees, in the water, and in the air.

Food-getting and locomotion are aspects of living which are important for the survival of the individual animal. But Nature also seems to take care of survival of the race by endowing each species with adaptations which are concerned with the birth of new animals, their care until able to fend for themselves, the construction of homes in which the young can be raised. Family life brings with it instruction of the young, defense against enemies, relaxation by play activities, and social behavior. In this, as in individual survival, mammals have a distinct advantage over their vertebrate relatives by a combination of giving birth to living young and a superior brain, making possible intelligent behavior.

Scientists who have studied the record of past forms of life preserved as fossils, inform us that when mammals first appeared they had to compete with the reigning dynasty of the huge reptiles. Most of the mammals were so small they could be crushed under the foot of a dinosaur. It was the capacity for intelligent behavior which enabled the tiny but wily primitive mammals to outwit and outlive their reptile enemies. Today mammals reign, not because of their size, nor their armor, nor their physical strength, but because of their intelligence.

We know surprisingly little about the private lives of many of our native mammals. What we do know has been discovered by observant hunters, trappers, and woodsmen as well as by field biologists. In the zoo and the laboratory we have learned much about the lives of a few selected species in captivity but their environment is an unnatural one. On the farm and in the home we have likewise learned a lot about a few domesticated animals, but again this environment is not natural. However, many biologists are now realizing the importance of obtaining more adequate knowledge of our native species in their natural haunts.

It may come as a surprise to learn that we know much less about mammal life than we do, for example, about birds or insects. Our knowledge of bird life has been gained largely through the efforts of a great number of enthusiastic bird watchers who, although amateurs, have contributed a great deal of information to the science of ornithology. We need a corresponding enthusiasm for "mammal watching." I hope this introduction to the lives of our mammals may encourage you to get acquainted with these interesting neighbors. By observing, recording and photographing what you discover, you may make a real contribution to the science of mammalogy. At the same time you will discover a thrilling, life-long hobby.

Clarence J. Hylander
Bel Air, Maryland
November, 1955

ANIMALS IN FUR

Many of the smaller species of mammals, such as these young raccoons, tolerate man and his activities, and often remain close to our homes.

CHAPTER ONE

MEET THE MAMMALS

Man has always felt a closer kinship with mammals than with any other group of animals. Because man himself is a mammal, the body and activities of mammals seem understandable to him. There are many other reasons for our greater familiarity with mammals than with other vertebrate groups. Since the dawn of civilization, man's progress has been closely bound to that of mammals. Some, either wild or domesticated, have always been our chief source of meat and milk. Others have been beasts of burden, essential to our agriculture and transportation. Many useful products such as leather and fur come from mammals. And last but not least, our two favorite family pets, the dog and the cat, are mammals. Their wild relatives in the United States, the coyote and the bobcat, can easily be mistaken for the domesticated species.

When man first came to this continent he found it a

paradise of mammals. Countless millions of fur-bearing animals roamed our virgin forests and prairies. Buffalo, deer, elk, moose, mink, and beaver were abundant where now they are practically extinct. The great carnivors could be found from coast to coast, where now the presence of a bear, wolf, puma, or wolverine makes headlines in the newspapers. But the flesh of mammals was meat for the colonists; their fur was a valuable trading commodity. When forests were cut over for lumber and agriculture, when large cities replaced pioneer towns, the mammals withdrew to more remote wilderness areas, their numbers decreasing with the advance of civilization. Only recently, as a result of a growing public demand for conservation of our wild life, have their numbers again begun to increase. Today many species have survived only through the protection afforded them in our wild-life refuges, national parks and forests.

This reduction in the numbers of many mammal groups, combined with their natural shyness and nocturnal habits makes it a rare treat for a field naturalist today to become acquainted with our larger mammals. However, many smaller species tolerate man and his activities, and at times even will become quite friendly. Unlike many animals in other groups, each mammal is an individualist; its behavior is unpredictable and often varies from that of any other member of the same species. Thus mammal-watching is always instructive and entertaining.

WHAT IS A MAMMAL?

Some people mistakenly think the words "animal" and "mammal" mean the same. They will say "we saw a number of birds, animals, and insects on our camping trip." But accurately the mammals are a special group within the animal kingdom.

A mammal is a vertebrate, or back-boned animal with certain internal and external features which set it apart from other vertebrates—the fishes, amphibians, reptiles, and birds. Many of these features can be observed only by close study of dead specimens and are of no value in identification and understanding of the mammals in nature. Certain features, however, are identification badges of a mammal; these distinguishing characteristics are a covering of hair or fur, the birth of living young, the presence of special glands in the skin, warm-blooded bodies, and a highly developed brain.

Mammals wear fur coats. The majority of mammals have hair or fur either on certain portions of the body or covering it completely. Even the elephant, the whale, and the manatee have remnants of hair on various parts of the body. Each hair is an outgrowth of the skin, a cylindrical shaft growing out of a pit and with its root a part of the hair follicle. Since each hair usually tapers toward the tip, animal fur tends to lie in one direction. In a few animals the hair tapers also at the base, so that the fur can be pushed either way; this accounts for the velvety softness of mole fur. The advantage to the mole is that it can move either forward or backward in its tight-fitting burrow without injury to the fur coat.

Each hair is provided with a muscle at its base, on the side opposite the slant of the hair. When this muscle contracts it makes the hair "stand on end." The stiffening of the fur on a cat's tail or a dog's neck is brought about in this way. We have inherited a similar mechanism in human skin which causes "goose flesh" when we are startled. In many mammals there are two kinds of hair, one forming smooth soft underfur and the other a stiffer covering of longer guard hairs. This is very noticeable in the muskrat.

Small areas of hair develop into special features as manes and fetlocks. In the porcupine some hairs become stiff and spine-like. At the opposite extreme is the hair which forms the soft wool of sheep. The bristles of hogs are stiff elastic hairs. In the cat family, sensitive hairs or feelers radiate from the nose; each stiff hair is seated in a special base from which nerves pass to the brain, carrying an impulse when the hair is disturbed.

Fur is important to a mammal since it traps dead air between the hair shafts, providing an insulating blanket for the skin. Fur coats make it possible for many mammals to remain active the year round, even under extremely cold and unfavorable weather conditions. The underfur of aquatic mammals also keeps the skin dry. Fur provides the distinctive coloring by which many mammals can be recognized, because it contains a brown pigment, known as melanin. When this pigment is so abundant that the fur looks black, the animal is known as a melanistic phase of the species. Many animals normally gray or brown have melanistic phases; among them is the black squirrel, which is really a melanistic gray squirrel, and the black jaguar. Absence of this pigment results in white fur, a condition known as albinism. Albino mammals are merely white phases of a normally colored animal, the best example being the domesticated white mouse and white rabbit. Few mammals are brightly colored; they lack the brilliant yellows, blues, greens, and reds of birds and reptiles.

Mammals give birth to living young. Mammals are a very successful group of animals, not only because of their fur coats but also because of their effective method of bringing their young into the world. Many hazards attend the hatching and later development of the unprotected young in egg-laying animals. The better the developing youngsters are protected the more successful the race is likely to be. What better protection than keeping the immature young within the mother's body until they are adequately developed! Many newly born mammals are actually able to move about and fend for themselves a few days after birth. All our native mammals have internal development of the young, within the mother's womb, where the embryo is nourished for weeks and even months. This is one of the unique distinctions of mammals as a group.

Mammals have special skin glands. The skin is a versatile part of the mammal's body. Not only does it produce hair, but also provides three special kinds of glands found only in mammals. Sweat glands, occurring in most species, give off water which has been removed from the blood stream; this water evaporates and thus cools the skin surface. Sweating is a cooling device of value to warm-blooded animals in summer. Another type is the oil gland located at the base of each hair which keeps the fur soft and pliable, an important condition for its usefulness. The most significant type of gland is the milk gland. Milk glands are so distinctive of mammals that their designation—mammary glands—gives the name to the whole group. Milk, one of the most nourishing foods known, is a food readily available to satisfy the urgent hunger of the rapidly growing young.

WHAT KINDS OF MAMMALS ARE NATIVE TO THE UNITED STATES?

A "kind" of animal or plant is known to the scientist as a species; all members of a species usually have so many traits in common, and these traits are so constantly passed on from one generation to the next, that all the individuals in the species look alike. In some biological sciences, notably mammalogy, the species is often subdivided into a number of varieties. Thus a "kind" of mammal is actually a particular variety as well as a particular species.

The most recent estimate of how many different kinds of mammals are native to the United States is given in the "List of North American Recent Mammals" published in 1955 by the United States National Museum. This lists approximately 3,622 species and varieties for the continent; the best guess is that 1,615 of these can be found in the United States. This may seem a large number of mammals, but actually it is a small part of the 20,000 different kinds of mammals of the world.

All these mammals are alike in the characteristics we have already described. Mammals vary among themselves however in a number of ways so that it is possible to recognize groups of species (genera and families). An important variation is the method by which the unborn young are nourished within the mother, and the degree of maturity they show when born. In the most advanced mammals a structure known as the placenta acts as a medium for food and air exchange between the embryo and the mother. Primitive mammals, such as the opossum, lack the placenta. Groups of mammals vary also in the

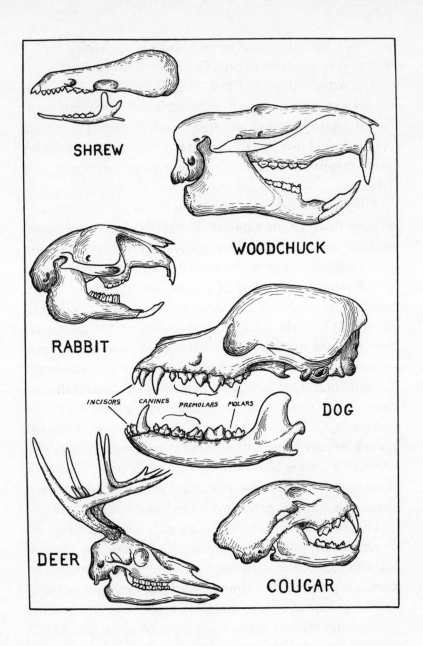

SHREW

WOODCHUCK

RABBIT

DOG

INCISORS CANINES PREMOLARS MOLARS

DEER

COUGAR

Adaptations of the Mammal Skull and Teeth.

ways in which their bodies and limbs are modified for life in different environments. The basic limb design is that of a quadruped, each limb terminating in digits whose tip is protected by a nail, claw, or hoof. The limbs vary in length, in number of digits, and in the type of toe protection. Thus the limb pattern has variations which make possible running, climbing, flying, swimming, and digging.

Another important variation in mammals is concerned with teeth and eating habits. The teeth of a typical mammal are differentiated into incisors in front, canines on either side of the incisors, and chewing teeth back in the cheek region consisting of premolars and molars. This can readibly be seen in a dog or cat, or even in our own mouth. When all of these teeth are about the same size, they are best suited for a mixed diet of plant and animal material; animals with such a diet are known as omnivors. In some mammal families the front teeth, especially the canines, are specialized for seizing and killing prey, and tearing flesh from bone; animals with such teeth are known as carnivors. Other families are vegetarians, with effective grinding teeth among the premolars and molars; these are the herbivors. A special group of herbivorous mammals, the rodents, have chisel-like incisor teeth.

The various families of mammals are identified by combinations of the above traits. Thus these are the features to look for in attempting to recognize mammals by name: type of limb, number of digits, presence of claws or hoofs, number and kinds of teeth. Usually smaller groups and species differ from each other in size and in color of their fur coats.

The Pouched Mammals

Known as marsupials, these are the most primitive group of mammals. The young are born in a very immature state, and spend their early babyhood in an external pouch of the mother's body. The brain of many marsupials is very simple, so that these species are unintelligent. The teeth also are simple. Marsupials reach their greatest development in Australia, where the best known member is the kangaroo. We have but one family (the *Didelphiidae*) with one species, the opossum, native to the United States.

The Insectivorous Mammals

This and all the following groups of mammals are characterized by a placenta in the development of the young. Insectivors are primitive, however, in tooth and brain development. They are small mouse-like animals which spend most of their lives underground.

The shrews (family *Soricidae*) are tiny soft-furred animals with sharply pointed snout and beady little eyes; their ears are hidden in the brown or gray fur. Shrews are often mistaken for mice, but a close look at the teeth reveals the difference. Shrews are insectivorous, with thirty-two small teeth; mice and related rodents have only twenty teeth and the incisors are prominent. Shrews, like moles, tunnel underground, are rarely encountered above ground. One of the species has the distinction of being the only mammal with a poisonous bite. The saliva contains a powerful poison which is injected into its prey by the bite of the shrew. Shrews fight each other and

-9-

attack even larger animals with surprising ferocity. About seventy different kinds occur in the United States.

Moles belong to the insectivor family *Talpidae*. They too are small mouse-like animals with plush-like fur which varies in color, on different species, from brown to silvery gray. The forelimbs of moles are marvelously adapted for use as shovels in excavating tunnels. Moles have tiny eyes and, although not blind, many species can only differentiate light from dark; since they spend most of their lives underground, eyesight would avail them little. Thirty-four kinds of moles live in the United States.

The Gnawing Mammals

The rodents, and their close relatives the rabbits and pikas, represent a most successful combination of mammal traits, if success is to be judged by the number of species and individuals. These animals are also the most widespread of all mammals, being found in every kind of habitat from ponds to tree-tops, and in every type of location from sea level to highest timberline. Their tooth specialization has given them a tremendous advantage over many other animals. The incisors, in reality self-sharpening chisels, can gnaw through the hardest material. These small and seemingly harmless mammals have such a fondness for all types of grain and seeds that they have become the number one enemy of the farmer.

The squirrel family (*Sciuridae*) with over two hundred varieties is a large group of rodents. Here we find the tree squirrels, ground squirrels, chipmunks, marmots, prairie dogs, and woodchucks. Some species are expert tree climbers, others are expert excavators. Two families are unusual in having external fur-lined cheek pouches which

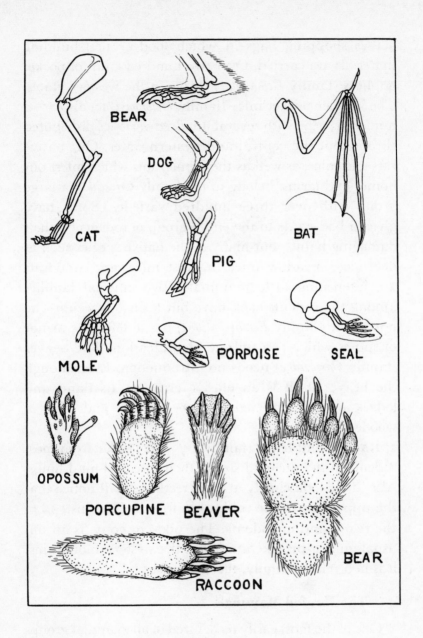

Adaptations of the Mammal Limb.

act as shopping bags in which food or nest-building materials are carried. Over two hundred kinds of pocket gophers (family *Geomyidae*) thrive in the western states. The smaller pocket mice (family *Heteromyidae*) also are a numerous tribe with several hundred varieties distributed throughout the central and western states. Our native rats and mice, as well as the immigrants which infest our homes and farms, belong to the family *Cricetidae,* a large group with over three hundred varieties. Some have given a bad name to the entire group of rodents by their damaging habits, but many of the native species such as deermice, meadow mice, harvest mice, and woodrats are interesting little mammals. Two unusual families among the rodents each have but a single species. The porcupine (family *Erethizontidae*) has a defensive armor of spines which is a unique identification. The beaver (family *Castoridae*) needs no introduction. Even though the beaver itself is an elusive creature, its dams and lodges are common sights in the streams and lakes of wooded country.

Rabbits and hares (family *Leporidae*) differ from most rodents in the unequal size of their fore and hind limbs. Also, if we look closely at their teeth, we will notice that the upper jaw of the rabbit has four incisors instead of the two found in rodents. The pika, or cony, is an unusual guinea-pig-like animal of the western mountains; it is in a related family, the *Ochotonidae*.

The Hoofed Mammals

One of the most easily recognized of all mammal groups is that of the hoofed mammals in which the toenail is modified to form a hoof, facilitating speedy travel over the ground. These mammals are also provided with grinding teeth suited for herbivorous eating habits. All our native hoofed animals have either two or four toes, and thus belong to the even-toed hoofed mammals. The first toe is missing; the second and fifth have either disappeared or are small useless appendages (dewclaws) which do not even touch the ground; the third and fourth toes are those which bear the hoofs. The hoofed animals are also distinctive in bearing horns or antlers.

The hoofed animals native to the United States belong to three families. In the deer family (*Cervidae*) the species bear antlers of solid bone which are shed every year. In this family we find the well-known game animals; deer, elk, and moose. A single species, the pronghorn antelope, belongs to the antelope family (*Antilocapridae*); it has unusual branching horns which are hollow sheaths on a bony core, and the horns but not the core are shed annually. The cattle family (*Bovidae*) is also known for its hollow horny sheaths on a bony core, but these are permanent throughout the life of the individual. Buffalo, mountain goat, and bighorn sheep are our wild cattle. Members of this family are also known as ruminants because they have a peculiar four-chambered stomach in which large amounts of food can be hastily stored, to be later regurgitated and digested at leisure.

The Carnivors

The meat-eaters, or carnivors, have specialized in preying on other animals for food. They have sharply clawed toes, powerful neck and shoulder muscles, dagger-like canine teeth, and shearing cheek teeth. In addition, carnivors are gifted with more than usual mammal intelligence; most of them are crafty hunters, capable of stalking animals much larger than themselves. Unlike the herbivors, whose meals need little skill or strength in the taking, carnivors must be swift, strong, and wily if they are not to starve. Five families of carnivors are found in the United States.

The weasel family (*Mustelidae*) is the largest group of carnivors, with over ninety varieties. They are small to medium-sized animals with short legs and supple bodies. Scent glands are highly developed in some species, as anyone knows who has encountered an angry skunk. Another familiar member of the family is the weasel. Less commonly encountered are the mink, badger, marten, fisher, otter, and the rare wolverine. The raccoon is the only common species in the raccoon family (*Procyonidae*).

The dog family (*Canidae*) is readily recognized by its resemblance to the domesticated dog; some of the wild species and their young can easily be mistaken for dogs. The legs are long, and the toes have fixed claws. The jaws are equipped with a complete set of incisors, canines, premolars, and molars. In this family are the fox, wolf, and coyote. Members of the cat family (*Felidae*) have jaws provided with longer and sharper canine teeth and more efficient meat-shearing cheek teeth. Unlike the dogs, the toes have retractile claws. Our wild cats are the lynx, bobcat, mountain lion, ocelot, and jaguar.

The largest carnivors are found in the bear family (*Ursidae*). The thick-set bodies are supported by short stout legs; bears walk flat-footed, after the fashion of humans. The teeth are not specialized for reliance on meat diet alone. The family includes the black bear and the grizzly bear.

The Flying Mammals

Bats are the only mammals which have achieved true flight; the so-called flying squirrels are really gliding animals which can take off from a high perch and soar to a lower one. Bats can fly because their body weight has been reduced to a minimum, and their forelimbs have become the light but strong framework of wings. The arm bones and fingers are tremendously elongated, and between them the skin forms a wing surface. Most of our common bats belong to the insect-eating family, *Vespertilionidae.* Being flying animals, bats are widely distributed throughout the United States.

The Aquatic Mammals

Mammals exhibit a wide range of adaptations for water-living, from the amphibious muskrat and beaver to the sleek otter which seems as much at home underwater as a seal. In fact, the completely aquatic mammals are so fish-like in appearance that some of them can understandingly be mistaken for fish. Yet mammals must breathe by means of lungs and, as a result, cannot stay underwater indefinitely. Adaptations for living in the water include reducing the fur coat to a light plush covering or eliminating it entirely. In some species the teeth have disappeared since they are not needed in an ocean filled with nourishing food which can be eaten as effortlessly as we eat soup. The body outline has been streamlined. But the most obvious changes have been in the limbs. Inside each flipper is the bony framework, common to all mammals; in the seals the toes are webbed. In one family, the *Otariidae,* small ears are visible; this family includes the sea lion and the fur seal. In the other family, the *Phocidae,* there are no external ears; this family includes the common harbor seal.

The most perfectly adapted of all mammals to life in the water are the whales. The fish-like form, the paddle-like forelimbs, the lack of hindlimbs, the horizontally flattened tail, all are changes suiting the animal for aquatic existence. Under the practically hairless skin lies a thick layer of blubber. In the whalebone whales, the usual mammalian teeth have been replaced by plates of whalebone. In this group of toothless whales we find the huge sulphur-bottom whale, the right whale, and the common finback whale. In another group of whales, known as the toothed whales, the jaws have retained their teeth. One family includes the porpoises and dolphins (the *Delphinidae*), which are often mistaken for fish.

WHERE CAN MAMMALS BE FOUND?

All the mammals described in this book cannot be found in any one place in the United States. A few species seem to thrive in a wide range of living conditions; these may be found in a great majority of our states. But most mammals have such preferences for a distinct type of home that they live only in certain areas. This distribution is what lends interest to a trip anywhere in the United States. New mammal neighbors can be discovered wherever you go. The following brief survey of the distribution of our native mammals may be helpful in knowing in advance where to expect certain kinds of mammals.

Whether you live on the Atlantic or the Pacific coast,

or in any of the states between, you can expect to encounter a shrew, mole, or bat. Among the rodents and their relatives there are a number of coast-to-coast members: chipmunk, cottontail rabbit, deermouse, meadow mouse, woodrat, muskrat, and beaver. The raccoon and weasel are other widely distributed mammals. Most cosmopolitan of all is the striped skunk, which you can be sure of finding almost anywhere.

If you live in the northeastern portion of the country, a ramble in the fields and woods may bring you face to face with a great number of rodents: several kinds of squirrels, woodchuck, porcupine, muskrat, deermice, meadow mice, jumping mice, and beaver. The only common hoofed mammal in this region is the white-tailed deer; moose is found only in inaccessible wilderness areas. Carnivors are more abundant: weasel, mink, otter, red fox, gray fox, and bobcat.

Southward along the Atlantic coast and in Florida occur some of the more northern mammals, but in fewer numbers. New species appear: fox squirrel, opossum, rice rat, cotton rat, and woodrat. The cottontail has as relatives the marsh rabbit and the swamp rabbit. Gray fox, skunk, and bobcat can be found. In the wilderness portions of Florida and nearby states roam white-tailed deer, black bear, and mountain lion. Transplanted colonies of armadillo have established themselves in the state, and the rare manatee inhabits the river estuaries.

In the grassy plains of the central states, rodents and rabbits hold full sway. Prairie dogs and pocket gophers are a special attraction of the wide open spaces. There is also a variety of pocket mice, ground squirrels, jumping mice, kangaroo rats, woodrats, and jack rabbits. The once wide-ranging buffalo is now found only in national parks and game refuges. Opossum, weasel, mink, skunk, and otter live where suitable habitats exist. The dog family is well represented by the coyote, as well as by the red fox, kit fox, and gray fox.

The heat and dryness of the Southwest, from Texas to California, presents an inhospitable environment for mammal life. Yet even here we find some old acquaintances and discover new ones. The sunbaked earth is honeycombed with the burrows of ground squirrels, pocket gophers, kangaroo rat, pack rat, and white-footed mouse. Desert carnivors include skunk, weasel, badger, fox, coyote, bobcat, and mountain lion. The jaguar and ocelot, strange cats from Mexico, roam into southern Texas and New Mexico. Here the armadillo has its native home.

In the Rocky Mountains and the far West we find a remnant of the mammal paradise which once included the entire country. Here we can find marmots, ground squirrels, pocket gophers, and pocket mice. Jack rabbits thrive in the lowlands and the strange pika in the mountains. Hoofed mammals are in their glory, with an abundance of deer, elk, moose, antelope, bighorn sheep, and mountain goat. Their numbers are kept in check by a great variety of carnivors: weasel, fox, coyote, timber wolf, mountain lion, lynx, black bear, and grizzly bear. The many national parks and forests in this region provide safe refuge for many of the vanishing species. Some of these "steal the show," for tourists who visit the national parks prefer to watch the antics of a bear and its cubs to viewing the grandeur of the scenery.

HOW DO MAMMALS VARY IN SIZE?

It is difficult to gain a correct idea of the size of a mammal from illustrations, since it is usually necessary to enlarge the smaller species in order to see the identifying details, and to greatly reduce the larger species. Thus before taking leave of the mammals as a group it might be worth while to compare the sizes of our common mammals.

The smallest mammal can curl up in the palm of your hand, and weighs but a fraction of an ounce. The largest mammal can overturn a boatload of fishermen. No other group of vertebrates exhibits such a tremendous range in size among its species. These differences are so great that the weight of some species is usually given in ounces, others in pounds, and still others in tons. The smallest mammals are those which fly or spend most of their lives as subterranean hermits. The medium-sized species are those which roam the surface of the earth. The giants are found among the sea-going mammals where huge bulk can be supported by the buoyancy of the water.

The smallest mammal is the pigmy shrew. Only a few inches in length, this diminutive animal weighs about one-fourteenth of an ounce. Other kinds of shrew range in weight from one-twelfth to one-half an ounce. Moles are also tiny mammals; their body length varies from three to five inches, their weight is usually less than five ounces. Adult grasshopper mice, deermice, and jumping mice tip the scales at about two ounces. Pocket gophers average four or five ounces. This small size does not necessarily mean a retiring disposition; some of the most ferocious killers are the shrews and grasshopper mice.

A flying mammal must conform to the same rules as those followed by aeronautical engineers in designing aircraft. There is a fixed relation between weight of the craft and wingspread. For this reason flying animals are characterized by a minimum of body weight; this is as true of mammals as of birds. Most bats weigh less than one ounce; since the fur covering the bat's body obscures its small size, the weight seems surprisingly little. The little brown bat, with a twelve-inch wingspread, weighs less than one-third of an ounce. Even the big brown bat with a five-inch body weighs less than an ounce.

As might be expected, most of the tree-climbing mammals are small, since excessive weight would be a handicap in the life of an aerial acrobat. Flying squirrels weigh about six ounces in spite of a fur-covered body six inches in length. The active little chipmunk is also in the featherweight class, rarely weighing more than five ounces. Other tree climbers are more heavily built. Red squirrels may weigh a pound, gray squirrels a pound and a half. The opossum, which grows to a length of twenty inches attains a weight of ten pounds. Porcupines are the lumbering heavyweights among the tree climbers, growing to a length of several feet and weighing up to a plump twenty pounds.

The professional hunters among the carnivors—the weasels and their relatives—are lean sinewy animals ranging in weight from one to twelve pounds. Also in the bantamweight class are the foxes (six to fifteen pounds) and the coyote (twenty to fifty pounds). Heavyweights among the carnivors are not numerous as to species, but they have played a picturesque role in our wild life, and have been the objective of human hunters as game animals. A wolf may weigh as much as seventy-five pounds. The ocelot is thirty-five pounds of muscle and stamina. Jaguar and mountain lions may weigh two hundred pounds or more. Bears are the champion heavyweights among the carnivors. The black bear, though only five feet in length, may weigh five hundred pounds; the larger grizzly bear has been known to attain eight hundred pounds.

Hoofed animals must rely on their fleetness of foot to escape the hungry carnivors, and as a rule do not carry excess weight. Deer, in spite of their five or six feet of length, rarely weigh more than two hundred pounds. Pronghorn antelope keep their weight down to a trim one hundred pounds. Elk are much bigger, with an overall length of nine feet and with weights up to seven hundred pounds. The real heavyweights among our land mammals are the moose and buffalo. Full-grown moose may be ten feet in length, weigh up to half a ton; buffalo bulls grow to eleven feet in length and weigh up to a ton.

The ocean is usually considered the undisputed domain of the fishes, yet the giants of the deep are mammals, not fish. In fact the mightiest animal ever to appear on earth, not excepting the dinosaurs, are the whales. A giant among giants is the sulphur-bottom, or blue, whale whose ninety feet of length measures a body weighing over one hundred tons. Imagine an animal so huge that its baby at birth is sixteen feet long and weighs more than a fullgrown buffalo!

From pigmy shrew to sulphur-bottom whale is a breathtaking range in size. Yet both animals are constructed on the same body plan, demonstrating the remarkable adaptability of the mammal pattern.

A black-tailed prairie dog surveys his surroundings for signs of danger before leaving the safety of his burrow.

CHAPTER TWO

THE GNAWING MAMMALS

Two thirds of all the different kinds of mammals in the United States gnaw their way through life. These animals have staked their chance for survival on their incisor teeth, which serve not only as chisels by which they secure their food and build their homes but also as weapons with which they fight their enemies. These clever mammals are miners, engineers, and architects of no mean ability. Being industrious members of our wild-life community, they spend endless hours in search for food, hoarding in hidden storehouses for future use whatever they do not eat on the spot. Their herbivorous appetite makes them a menace to agriculture; but fortunately, in the balance of nature, their numbers are kept within bounds by carnivorous mammals, birds, and reptiles.

The first animal you encounter on a nature walk will undoubtedly be one of the gnawing mammals: usually a squirrel or a rabbit. Few are unusual in size or appearance, but closer observation of their habits will increase your admiration for these animals which survive in spite of such incredible odds. They hold their own by being able to live in environments and on food materials which are overlooked by other mammals, and by maintaining an exceptionally high birth rate. In many species one pair can have over sixty children, grandchildren, and great grandchildren in a single year!

Of the gnawing animals, the rodents have in common four prominent incisor teeth, two in the upper jaw and two in the lower. In the rabbit family an additional pair of small incisors is located behind the upper pair. Canine teeth are absent, leaving a toothless space between the incisors and the chewing teeth. The incisors wear away faster on the inside than the outside so that the cutting edge is always chisel-sharp. Powerful muscles move the lower jaw so that gnawing animals can cut through such material as hard-coated seeds, wood, and even good-sized trees.

These mammals have made themselves at home in a variety of habitats. Many species are expert diggers, using teeth and claws to excavate underground highways and homes. Their compact bodies are modified for such a life by a shortened neck, short legs, and small ears and eyes. Others have become the sprinters of the animal world, with long hind legs which enable them to cover the ground in great leaps and bounds. Some are expert climbers, using the tree tops for their homes and feeding grounds. All are good swimmers, but a few are specially suited for life in the water by having webbed feet and waterproof underfur.

TREE SQUIRRELS AND CHIPMUNKS

GRAY SQUIRREL.   This friendly mammal is one of our few animal neighbors which has completely adjusted itself to civilization, making itself at home in city parks and around dwellings. Its gray or brownish fur coat and large bushy tail are a familiar sight. Gray squirrels were once much more numerous than they are now. A migration in Wisconsin in 1842 lasted four weeks and included an estimated 500,000,000 individuals. Today gray squirrels are found wherever there are woods from New England to Minnesota and southward to Louisiana. They are most active for a short time in the early morning and late afternoon.

During spring and summer their diet consists of berries, fruit, insects, and additional delicacies such as flowers and mushrooms. In winter they rely on their buried stores of nuts, acorns, and seeds. A gray squirrel may have several homes: a den in a hollow tree, and leafy nests among the branches in the trees. The leaf nests are very conspicuous in winter when the trees are bare. Young squirrels are born in late winter or early spring, each litter usually consisting of triplets and quadruplets. Baby squirrels may remain with their mother through the first winter. They can expect to live for eight more years, if lucky enough to escape hunters and their many carnivorous enemies. Gray squirrels do not hibernate, but in cold or rainy weather they stay in their nests, sometimes for weeks at a time. They venture forth when hungry, looking for the hidden caches where they had buried food when it was plentiful.

The eastern gray squirrel has several relatives. The WESTERN GRAY SQUIRREL, a slightly larger species with narrower tail and dusky feet, is found in California and Oregon. In the Southwest lives the ARIZONA GRAY SQUIRREL with black on its tail. But the beau brummel of the family is the TASSEL-EARRED SQUIRREL of the yellow-pine forests of Arizona and Colorado. These beautiful squirrels, when wearing their winter costume, have tufts of hair on their ears. One kind of tassel-earred squirrel lives along the south rim in Grand Canyon National Park; it has a reddish brown band along the back, white belly clearly marked off from the gray sides, and a gray tail which is white on the underside. Another variety, found nowhere else in the world, frequents the north rim of the Park. Also known as the Kaibab squirrel, it is strikingly attired in a black "vest" and a pure-white bushy tail.

RED SQUIRREL. Although smallest of the tree squirrels, the red squirrels are the noisiest members of the forest community. When not scolding at an intruder they are chattering to themselves continuously. Red squirrels are suspicious even of each other, and often quarrel among themselves. They seldom tolerate gray squirrels in the same territory; in fact they chase their bigger but less belligerent relatives out of their domain. The red squirrel actually has a rusty-brown fur coat with grayish sides, and is marked by a black line from shoulder to hip.

Red squirrels make their homes in the evergreen forests of northeastern United States, but are sometimes found in woods of mixed deciduous and evergreen trees; they occur as far south as the mountains of South Carolina and west to the woods of Minnesota. Like the gray squirrels they are daytime explorers, constantly on the search for seeds and nuts. They particularly like to cut down green cones and stock-pile huge quantities of them around a stump or boulder, selecting a damp shaded spot where the cones will not ripen too quickly. Such piles may contain eight to ten bushels of cones. Red squirrels sometimes feed on insects and, unfortunately for those who wish to have birds around their homes, they rob birds' nests of their eggs. If you have come across mushrooms fastened to the lower branches of a tree, you may have wondered why they were there. Red squirrels consider mushrooms a delicacy, and string them on the branches to dry; poisonous mushrooms have no harmful effect on them.

Red squirrels live in holes in stumps and logs, in leaf nests, and in underground shelters. The young, usually three or four in a litter, are born in May and June. During cold spells, squirrel families hide but they do not hibernate. Their natural enemies are those of all squirrels: weasel, mink, hawk, owl, and blacksnake. Five years is the natural life span of the red squirrel.

The common eastern red squirrel has two relatives in the West. The CHICKAREE, or Douglas squirrel, lives in the fir and spruce forests of the Pacific coast; it has a rusty rather than whitish belly and a tail fringed with white. The PINE SQUIRREL of the yellow-pine forests of the southern Rocky Mountains has white underparts as well as a white-fringed tail.

FOX SQUIRREL. This is the largest American tree squirrel. Full-grown individuals reach a length of over two feet and weigh three pounds. They show great individuality in their fur coats. Some are dark brown, even black; others are buff or gray; still others are brighter-hued yellowish or orange brown. In all cases the bushy, fox-like tail is frosted with white hairs. Fox squirrels are slow-moving deliberate animals more awkward in trees than their smaller relatives. This species can be found throughout eastern United States south of Pennsylvania and west to the Mississippi River valley; they prefer open woods to dense forests. During summer they eat fruits, berries, bulbs, buds, and bark. At other times they rely upon acorns, nuts, and seeds. Nuts are buried in separate small holes in the ground, to be dug up when needed. Fox squirrels not only are beautiful animals, but, being of a gentle disposition, make good pets.

FLYING SQUIRREL. The gray or reddish brown fur coat of this would-be aviator is velvety soft, with spotlessly white underparts. On each side of the body, folds of fur-covered skin extend from the forelimbs to the hindlimbs. When the squirrel takes off from a tree, it spreads its limbs and the taut skin-folds serve as "wings." A flying squirrel is not a true flier, but an accomplished glider, able to soar a hundred feet or more. Two species are native, both alike in having the large eyes of all nocturnal animals. The northern flying squirrel is found in the evergreen forests of the northeastern states and the Northwest; it is the larger of the two species, growing to a length of twelve inches. The smaller southern flying squirrel prefers oak and hickory forests and is found from New England to Florida and Texas.

Flying squirrels sleep during the day and are active at night. They eat nuts, seeds, berries, and fruits; but in addition are somewhat carnivorous, enjoying a meal of

A flying squirrel has the large eyes typical of animals which sleep during the day and are active at night.

small birds and their eggs, and nibbling at meat supplies left unprotected in summer camps. The den of a flying squirrel is often an old woodpecker's hole or similar hollow in a tree, in which a bed is made of shredded bark and lichens. They are sociable animals; as many as fifty individuals have been found living together in one large den. Their soft chirping sounds remind one of birds; when alarmed they utter louder squeaks and squeals. Flying squirrels are friendly animals, but when kept as pets they should be handled carefully, for their frail bodies are easily injured.

EASTERN CHIPMUNK. The call of the chipmunk is a sharp "chip-chip-chip" which is responsible for its name. Although considered a tree squirrel, the chipmunk spends much of its time on the ground or in an underground den. It is a trim and smartly dressed animal in reddish brown fur coat striped with black and white; the tail is flattened, not bushy like that of the squirrels. The single eastern species has a wide distribution through the woods of eastern United States, south to the mountains of Georgia and west to the Mississippi River. Chipmunks are a strange mixture of shyness and curiosity, one moment on the verge of accepting advances, the next dashing for the safety of a rock crevice or hollow log.

Chipmunks enjoy a drink of water now and then, and thus often locate their dens near the edge of a pond or stream. They spend the nights in their underground rooms, but bestir themselves at dawn to forage for their favorite seeds and berries. They cram what food they can collect into their internal cheek pouches until they bulge to the bursting point. Some of this food is carried to underground storehouses, some scattered in small holes dug in the ground, and some deposited even under the mattress of leaves in the chipmunk's bedroom. The sleepy chipmunk can turn over, reach under the bed, and have a snack whenever it gets hungry.

A chipmunk's babies are twins or triplets born in April. When three months old the little chipmunks begin to shift for themselves. Young and old however must be constantly on watch for their blood-thirsty enemies—weasels, owls, and snakes. Their only defense is speedy flight to the nearest safe hiding place. In the North they retire to their cozy dens about November first, spending long periods in sleep, waking when hungry and then feasting on their hoarded food. In the southern states the chipmunks remain active the year round.

The WESTERN CHIPMUNK is a smaller animal, gray rather than rusty brown, and with more delicate and more numerous stripes. One species lives in the alpine environment of the Sierra Nevada mountains at altitudes of 12,000 feet. Other species live on the sagebrush plains, in the evergreen forests of the Northwest, and among the yellow pines of the Rocky Mountains.

GROUND SQUIRRELS, MARMOTS, AND PRAIRIE DOGS

In contrast to the tree squirrels, ground squirrels spend much of the time on the ground or hidden in their underground apartments. Many have such greedy appetites that they spend most of their waking hours eating; at other times they are content to sleep or hibernate. Over a hundred varieties of ground squirrel are found throughout central and western United States. Of the marmot species the only eastern representative is the woodchuck. Ground squirrels, marmots, and prairie dogs can often be seen sitting upright, stiff as ramrods, on the alert for danger. Their hearing is very acute, so that it takes only a slight sound to send them scurrying into their burrows. The smaller species are ten to eleven inches in length, the larger reach nineteen inches. Many of the species look like slender gray squirrels, others resemble chipmunks, still others are distinctively marked such as the striped ground squirrel and the golden-mantled squirrel.

STRIPED GROUND SQUIRREL. This prairie dweller, also known as the thirteen-lined squirrel, is found over a large portion of central United States, west to Montana and south to Texas. Striped ground squirrels wear brown fur coats conspicuously marked by numerous lengthwise white stripes, some with rows of black spots. This ground squirrel eats seeds and nuts, but in addition has a liking for grasshoppers, mice, eggs, and young birds. They are active throughout the day, seemingly unaffected by the noonday heat of the prairie. When they invade agricultural regions they become quite a pest, but normally their numbers are kept in check by such natural enemies as coyotes, weasels, and snakes. Striped ground squirrels excavate burrows for their homes; by August they are fat from continuous eating, and then retire to these dens. Here they spend five or six months in hibernation, during which an individual may wake once in a while but does not venture above ground until the following spring.

ANTELOPE SQUIRREL. This wary chipmunk-like animal of the Southwest has a buff-colored fur coat which blends inconspicuously into the color tones of the desert background. A single lengthwise white stripe on each side differentiates this species from the chipmunk. It feeds on seeds of yucca, cactus, mesquite, and pinon. Like many other desert rodents it can stand high temperatures, even such as are found in Death Valley, California, where the thermometer sometimes reaches 130°F. in the shade. Antelope squirrels are active during the early morning and late afternoon hours; they retire to their comfortable air-conditioned burrows for a midday siesta and again for the night. They do not hibernate but live on their supply of stored food during the winter months, when nature provides them with an extra-thick coat of underfur to keep them warm.

GOLDEN-MANTLED GROUND SQUIRREL. In the pine and aspen forests of the western mountains

Some Common Members of the Squirrel Family.

lives this friendly short-limbed rodent which wears a "mantle" of golden brown on the back of its head and shoulders. Elsewhere the coat is dark gray or buff, marked by a stripe extending from shoulder to hip, edged with black on each side. These little mammals are a feature attraction in many of the western national parks. They sit erect and beg so appealingly for food that tourists comply too generously; by late summer the well-fed squirrels can hardly waddle about. Their natural food is berries, nuts, seeds, and insects. Golden-mantled ground squirrels go into hibernation in September, remaining so until the following April.

COLUMBIAN GROUND SQUIRREL. The largest member of the ground-squirrel group, this species lives on the sparsely wooded slopes of Montana, Idaho, Oregon, and Washington where it feeds on bulbs, flowers, fruits, and juicy foliage. Because of its liking for crops, this squirrel has added man to the list of its natural enemies, the coyotes, bears, and wolves. Columbian ground squirrels start a long hibernation period as soon as they are well fattened, sometimes as early as July. They emerge in February from their hibernation dens under the ground, often having to dig their way out to face a cold and bleak early spring. During this critical period they rely on the food which they stored away the previous summer.

YELLOW-BELLIED MARMOT. Marmots are larger, more stocky rodents than the ground squirrels; their bodies are heavy, their legs short, and their heads are flattened. They are noted for their unusual whistling ability; in fact the Canadians call one kind of marmot "whistling pig." The yellow-bellied marmot is the smallest member of the tribe, but even this marmot grows to twenty inches in length and attains a weight of fifteen pounds. It is sometimes known as rock-chuck, because of the habit of locating a home among the rocks and boulders. The fur is grayish or brown, the face marked with a white band between the eyes. It is active only for three or four months of the year, the other months being spent in hibernation. This marmot is quite sociable and mingles with other individuals of its kind; sometimes large groups live in villages, prairie-dog fashion. Yellow-bellied marmots post sentinels which sit on their haunches while watching for signs of danger. When an enemy appears, the marmot gives a piercing whistle as a signal.

HOARY MARMOT.   This black and white marmot, with black-booted feet, is the champion whistler of the clan. At the approach of a feathered divebomber in the form of an eagle or a hawk, it lets loose such shrill blasts that the sound sends all the wild animals within hearing scrambling for safety. Colonies of these marmots become very noisy, since one of their favorite activities is conducting championship whistling matches. Hoary marmots live in rocky places near timberline in Idaho and Washington.

WOODCHUCK.   Known also as ground hog, this is an animal with its own day on the calendar. Candlemas Day, February 2, was an early Christian festival in Europe; the weather on that day was supposed to be very significant. According to a seventeenth-century English proverb,

> If Candlemas Day be fair and bright,
> Winter will have another flight;
> If on Candlemas Day it be shower or rain,
> Winter is gone and will not come again.

No one knows how or why the European hedgehog, and also the badger, came to fill the role of weather prophet on that day. However, if one of these animals came out of its burrow and saw its shadow, it was supposed to return for another six-weeks' sleep, and winter would continue that much longer. When the early English settlers carried the tradition to this country, they selected the woodchuck to act the role of weather forecaster. Unfortunately for its reputation, careful check of the weather records on Ground Hog Day over a number of years shows the woodchuck to be a very unreliable weather prophet.

The woodchuck is a familiar figure, sitting erect at the entrance to its burrow or peering above the roadside grasses. Like the gray squirrel, it is one of the few remaining mammals seen frequently in populated areas. The word "woodchuck" is considered by some naturalists to be an American version of the Indian name "otchoek." The coarsely furred, brownish rodent likes to locate its underground home near fields of cultivated crops. It is rarely found more than a hundred yards from the entrance to its burrow. Woodchucks eat berries, bark, some insects, and snails; they have a special fondness for apples. The eastern woodchuck occurs across all of Canada from Newfoundland to Alaska; it has spread south of the border into the United States as far as Maryland and the Mississippi River valley.

Woodchucks go into hibernation in August, usually when they are so fattened by summer gorging that they can scarcely move. They emerge again in March, barring a possible peek at the world on Ground Hog Day! The annual litter of three or four is born in April or May.

While still nursing, the babies are often fed choice morsels brought into the burrow by the mother. Woodchucks utter the typical marmot whistle, but also give muffled barks and a variety of squeals when fighting.

PRAIRIE DOG.   The name of this rodent, like the common names of many other wild animals, is a misnomer. To the first explorers of the great plains, this animal, sitting up pertly and holding its small forepaws against its chest, may have looked from a distance like a dog. Or the name may have come from its bark-like yipping. Be that as it may, the name is now widely used. The prairie dog is a plump animal with a sandy-brown fur coat which blends well with the dry grass and earth of its environment. A full-grown "dog" measures about twelve inches in length and weighs some two pounds. There are two common species. The black-tailed prairie dog inhabits the vast reaches of the central states from the Mississippi River west to Texas. The white-tailed prairie dog, a more slender animal with shorter tail, lives farther west in the Rocky Mountains, from Wyoming to Arizona.

Prairie dogs are the most sociable of all mammals. They live in underground communities which inspired the wonder tales of early explorers. In 1900 one "dog town" was known to extend for 250 miles and was estimated to have a population of 400,000,000 individuals! A prairie dog excavates tunnels and subterranean chambers with its sharp claws, kicking the dirt by backward strokes of the hind feet. When not busy digging or eating, a prairie dog stays above ground squatting on its haunches and surveying the world; it is never far from the burrow's front door. When alarmed the prairie dog darts for home; but before disappearing, prompted by curiosity, it will pause, sit erect, and watch developments until the last possible moment. Then it dashes quickly out of sight.

Prairie dogs are hearty eaters, consuming large quantities of grass and other vegetation. This appetite has not endeared them to farmers, since prairie dogs can seriously deplete the food supply of grazing animals. After a summer's feeding, prairie dogs grow fat and finally retire for a long sleep during the winter months. During periods of warm weather some individuals come above the ground, so that a few prairie dogs can be seen during every month of the year. Their chief natural enemies are badger, coyote, and various birds of prey. In nature a prairie dog is lucky to live for eight years; in captivity some have grown to be ten years old.

POCKET GOPHERS

POCKET GOPHER. This group of gnawing mammals includes a number of species of stout burrowing rodents which seem a cross between an overgrown mole and a small prairie dog. Their name refers to unusual slits found on the outside of the cheeks, which open into fur-lined pockets. These handy pouches, which can be filled by the forepaws, can be turned inside out to be cleaned, and then pulled back into place by special muscles. Pocket gophers are well equipped for being miners. Powerful incisor teeth and large front claws are their digging tools. Pocket gophers have small eyes and ears, a short neck, and a compact cylindrical body. The fur varies from creamy white to gray or brownish black in different individuals; the color often duplicates that of the soil in a particular species' home.

Numerous species of western pocket gophers inhabit the prairies, open woodlands, and deserts from the Dakotas to Texas and west to the Pacific coast. Their length varies from nine to twelve inches. Rarely seen by day, they become active at night searching for their favorite roots, bulbs, and other vegetable material. The eastern pocket gopher has brown or black fur, and is about the same size as its western relative. It can be found as far east as the Gulf states and Florida. The tail of this rodent serves as an organ of touch, enabling the animal to back up in the narrow tunnels and yet feel its way along. On the whole, it is a solitary and silent creature of the underground.

The gopher seems loathe to leave its burrow, acting as if it wanted to spend as little time as possible in the hostile world above ground. Even when feeding, it appears at the opening for only a second or two, often leaving its hind quarters inside the burrow as it reaches for food. Active both day and night, it has to be on constant guard against its enemies the hawks, owls, and snakes.

Pocket gophers are remarkably industrious excavators. One tunnel system dug by a single gopher was five hun-

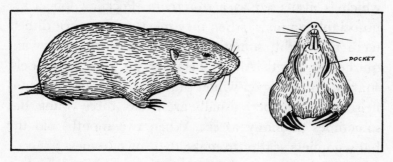

Pocket Gopher

dred feet long, and had a hundred mounds of excavated dirt along its extent. The dirt is brought to the surface at intervals and left in fan-shaped mounds. The entrance mounds are larger than molehills, and have the opening on the side. The rate of excavation per gopher is remarkable, sometimes being two hundred feet of tunnel per night. A man would have to dig a seventeen-inch trench seven miles long in ten hours to equal the nightly accomplishment of a one-pound gopher! The digging is done by downward strokes of the powerful front paws and claws, sweeping the dirt back under the belly and then kicking the pile to the rear with the hind feet. In hard soil the large upper incisors are used to loosen the gravel by powerful downward strokes; the lips close around and behind these teeth thus keeping dirt out of the mouth. When a large pile has accumulated the gopher turns a somersalt, faces the rear, and, with forepaws held on either side of the head, bulldozes the dirt to an opening. While digging, the ears are closed tight by valves and the eyes are protected by tightly shut eyelids.

An entire tunnel system is built by one animal, and used by the occupant as a means of going to new feeding grounds. Underground, the tunnel leads to a bedroom, which is also used as a storeroom. Pocket gophers are unsociable animals; when they meet, gophers grind their teeth and fight, sometimes so viciously that the vanquished is killed. All gophers are the prey of weasels, snakes, and badgers which pursue them into their tunnels. In a litter there usually are two or three young, but sometimes as many as six. When two months old the baby gophers scatter to make their own homes.

MICE AND RATS

When we think of rodents the animals which naturally come to mind are the rats and mice found in homes and other buildings. But all rats and mice are not the repulsive, destructive animals which have invaded our populated areas. Destruction of crops and food supplies, invasion of our homes with accompanying filth and damage, and transmission of diseases are brought about chiefly by European species which have come to this country as uninvited immigrants. They have overrun our cities because they will live under conditions which are unacceptable to most of our native species. Two of these rodents which have given a bad reputation to the whole group are the Norway rat and the house mouse.

The NORWAY RAT, or wharf rat, is rodent Public Enemy Number One; it is a coarse-furred, grayish brown animal with large naked ears and a scaly hairless tail. This rat often grows to a length of fifteen or eighteen inches. It thrives amid garbage and refuse in slums, around wharves, and in salt marshes. Because of their aggressive disposition, adaptable nature, and rugged physiques, wharf rats are able to drive out the less destructive native species.

The HOUSE MOUSE is a smaller grayish brown rodent with lighter-brown or buff underparts; it also has naked ears and a naked tail. Its average length is six or seven inches. In the northern states this mouse has become an indoor animal for most of the year, building nests of soft material in walls, attics, and cellars; but in summer it moves out into the fields. Like the rat, the house mouse will eat anything. It can be distinguished from similar native mice of the same size by the ashy underparts, dull colors, and naked or semi-naked tail. Meadow mice with similar color pattern have more robust bodies, longer fur, and shorter tail. White-footed mice have a different color pattern, and harvest mice are more slender with a proportionally longer tail. The white mice used as pets and laboratory animals are albino varieties of the house mouse.

In contrast to these introduced rodents, our native rats and mice are often attractive in appearance and intriguing in their habits. Only a few become destructive pests in agricultural areas. They grow unduly abundant only when the balance of nature is upset by unwise killing of the carnivors which feed on rodents and keep their numbers in check.

MEADOW MOUSE. Meadow mice are also known as field mice or voles. There are over a dozen species of this very common rodent, all difficult to tell apart. Meadow mice are stocky, short-eared mice with gray or brown fur coats, shading to slate or buff on the underparts; they vary in length from four to ten inches. Meadow mice have established themselves in grassy and weedy habitats, from lowland plains to mountain summits, across the entire northern half of the United States. An unusual feature which serves them well is the forehead which recedes above the bulging eyes so that the mice can see directly upward without tilting their heads. More frequently seen than the busy little animals themselves are their trails, miniature highways which form labyrinths among the grass jungles, the "pavement" worn smooth by countless thousands of tiny hurrying feet.

Meadow mice are energetic animals constantly on the go, day and night, relaxing only for a few hours at a time to nap in their private bedrooms. They are vegetarians, feeding on seeds, roots, leaves, and bark. Meadow mice are continually in search of something to eat and consume their weight in food every day. What they can't eat they carry to underground storerooms. Round holes along the runways lead to underground nests where the busy little rodents store food, sleep, and raise their families. A mother may have seventeen litters in one year. Since a litter may include four or five young which mature and have families of their own when four weeks old, the reproductive rate of these little animals is tremendous. The meadow-mouse population ordinarily is about fifty to one hundred

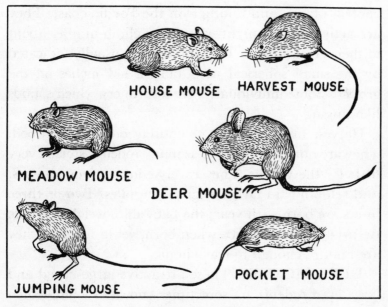

Some Common Mice.

individuals per acre, but it can be as high as 8000 per acre.

In winter, meadow mice build spherical nests woven of grass, above ground. They dislike warm weather; when summer temperatures rise above 85°F., they retreat to their cool underground quarters. Meadow mice are preyed upon by all the small carnivorous mammals, as well as by snakes, sea gulls, and marsh birds. The average field mouse survives little more than a year.

HARVEST MOUSE. These dainty little animals, seldom noticed because they have no conspicuous marking, could easily be mistaken for the common house mice. Harvest mice are clothed in a grayish or brown fur coat which shades to a lighter buff or gray on the sides, and white on the underside. Of the common species, one is found throughout eastern United States, another on the central plains, and another on the Pacific coast. They are active only at night when they climb nimbly about in their grass jungles. Their presence is usually indicated by the small spherical nests built a few inches off the ground. Some individuals have a shrill cry which sounds like singing.

Harvest mice rely almost entirely on seeds for food. They are not as foresighted as many rodents, storing very little for the winter. They rarely come into our homes, and seldom raid farmers' grain supplies. Two or three litters are born each year; the baby mice weigh only one twenty-fifth of an ounce when born, yet in ten days they are mature enough to leave home.

DEER MOUSE. These attractive large-eared and large-eyed rodents are sometimes known as white-footed mice; they have neat gray or brown fur coats clearly set off from the white underparts. They can readily be mistaken for overgrown house mice; but a close look will reveal the hairy rather than scaly tail, and the white vest and feet. The name deer mice is the result of the similarity of the color pattern to white-tailed deer. Numerous species, ranging in size from five to ten inches, are found in various parts of the country. The woodland deer mouse is found in all the eastern states except in the Southeast where it is replaced by the golden and cotton deer mice. The pinon and desert mice live in California and the Southwest. The long-tailed deer mouse is the largest species and has the widest range, inhabiting most of the United States.

Deer mice are agile nocturnal mice with a thin squeaky voice; their "song" is often likened to a high-sustained trill. When excited they make a drumming sound by thumping with their forepaws. They eat seeds, nuts, fruits, insects, and occasionally carcasses of small animals. Deer mice show great originality in their choice of homes. Some are spherical nests in low branches; others, short tunnels; still others are in abandoned burrows of other rodents. Hollow logs and old bird nests are also used.

GRASSHOPPER MOUSE. This is the killer of the mice family. Grasshopper mice are diminutive gray or brown carnivors which pounce on their prey and kill with sharp stabs of their incisor teeth. The common name refers to their fondness for grasshoppers; in some parts of the country they are known as scorpion mice because of a preference for these small animals. Grasshopper mice are night-time rovers of the grasslands from the Dakotas to Washington, south to the Mexican border. They live in burrows and holes in the ground, usually those dug by other rodents; they use these underground homes the year round. Grasshopper mice utter shrill cries which have been likened to a miniature wolf howl.

JUMPING MOUSE. The long hind legs and peculiar locomotion of this mouse are responsible for its other common name, kangaroo mouse. Jumping mice are sprightly and high-strung little animals weighing less than an ounce. For their size they are remarkable broad-jumpers, clearing ten to twelve feet in a single leap. If a man had the same proportionate propulsion energy for his weight, he would have to travel by single jumps of four and a half miles each! Since they are nocturnal, these interesting mice are rarely seen. The tiny body is covered with a yellowish brown fur coat marked by a darker brown stripe along the back from nose to tail. The tail is very long, sometimes more than half the body length; it serves as a counterbalance when the animal is jumping. Jumping mice live in woods, swamps, and meadows of the cooler portions of the United States, where they eat seeds, fruits, and insects. The home of a jumping mouse may be a shallow burrow used in winter for long periods of sleep, or a spherical nest for summer use hidden among the grasses.

POCKET MOUSE. Like the pocket gophers, these smaller rodents have external slits leading to fur-lined pouches in their cheeks. Pocket mice have broad large heads, large eyes and an unusually long tail; the hindlimbs are only slightly longer than the forelimbs. Their brown or grayish fur coat is lighter on the underparts. Numerous species are common in the arid habitats of the central and southwestern states. The Pacific pocket mouse is the smallest of the rodents.

Pocket mice lead a nocturnal existence, foraging at night for seeds, green parts of plants, juicy cactus pulp, and small insects. They are well fitted for life in an environment where water is scarce. They can go without drinking, due to an ability to manufacture what water they need within their own bodies from foods they eat. Having weak forelimbs, pocket mice can tunnel only in loose soil. They leave small round holes in the ground, which lead directly into their burrows. Gentle and harmless as far as man is concerned, they do not get along with each other and lead solitary lives. In nature they are preyed upon by badgers, coyotes, skunks, and foxes.

Many animals are protectively colored, so that in their normal environment they are inconspicuous and so escape attack by their enemies. If unusual colors do appear in some individuals of a species, these colors attract attention and the individuals are apt to be killed off; thus the survivors in a particular environment often come to look alike and exhibit the same protective coloring. This is strikingly shown by two varieties of pocket mice which live in New Mexico. The sands of White Sands National Monument are dazzling white gypsum; the pocket mice here are white, and they rarely venture far from the white sands. Forty miles away the soil is dark, since it is eroded black lava rock. Here the pocket mice are dark brown or black. The dark mice remain in their habitat and the light ones in theirs, where the color of the fur coat makes its owner inconspicuous.

WOODRAT. There are a number of species of this widely distributed native rat, which grows to a length of sixteen inches. The ears are large and hairy, the tail is hairy, and the eyes bulge. The even coloring of the gray, buff, or brown fur coat distinguishes the wood rats from the ground squirrels; the hairy tail and soft fur is different from that of the other common rats. All but one species are western, living on the open plains or in rocky woodlands. Woodrats venture out after dusk for their meal of berries, nuts, seeds, and grasses.

A fascinating western species is the PACK RAT, the only American mammal with an unquenchable collecting instinct. Inquisitive and impertinent by nature, it raids human habitations and picks up almost any object, particularly shiny and glittering ones. The pack rat often becomes a likeable nuisance in spite of its habit of carrying away anything from jewelry and cutlery to coins and false teeth. It is also known as a trade rat since, if its fancy is caught by a new object, the rat drops whatever it was carrying and leaves it in place of what it now steals. The rooms in its bulky nest are packed with plunder brought back from camps and prospectors' cabins.

Pack rats eat the soft parts of plants, cactus pulp, and any available fruits and seeds. The clumsily constructed home, resembling a beaver lodge on dry land, is made of a mass of branches; the hallways leading into the living quarters are often ingeniously lined with bits of thorny cactus, to discourage intruders. Far from being secretive, this nocturnal rodent is so noisy when it visits a camp or cabin that it often keeps the human occupants awake.

COTTON RAT. The habit of stealing fibers from the cotton bolls for lining its nest has given this rat of the southern farmlands its name. It thrives in the mild climate of southeastern United States. Similar in size and color to its companion the rice rat, the cotton rat has longer more grizzled fur and a shorter stouter tail. Its food is chiefly grasses and cultivated grains; it often damages sugar cane and sweet potato crops as well as truck gardens. Living in burrows and rock crevices of fields and roadsides, this rat forages for food every month of the year, rarely storing any. Its tremendous reproductive rate is kept in check by the alligators, water snakes, and owls which feed on cotton rats.

RICE RAT. When rice was an important crop in southeastern United States, this aquatic rat was a sufficient menace to merit its common name. It is fairly large, nine to twelve inches in length, with a gray or brownish fur coat, and light-gray feet and underparts. Rice rats live in marshes and wet lowlands from Virginia to Texas, building spherical nests in the grasses above high-water level and constructing conspicuous feeding platforms, on

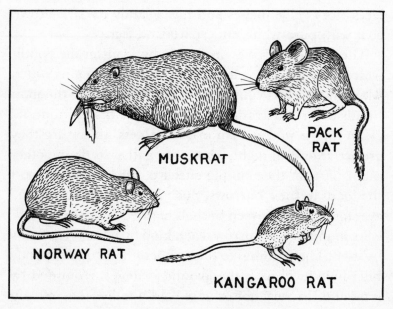

Some Common Rats.

which they sit and eat their meals. As might be expected, they swim and dive well. They subsist on a diet of vegetation and such aquatic animals as snails and crustaceans. Rice rats have large families, with eight or nine litters a year, each of four or five babies. Water moccasins, rattlesnakes, and owls, in addition to the usual small carnivors, prey on these swamp-dwelling rats.

KANGAROO RAT. This is actually a pocket mouse, with the fur-lined cheek pouches typical of the family. It has long hind legs and a long tail, tufted at the tip, which is used as a counterbalance or as a prop. Kangaroo rats travel by long leaps, not using the forelimbs at all, as if the hindlimbs were on coiled springs. They can spring vertically a foot or more into the air, twisting or dodging while aloft and thus often escaping the badger or fox which is pursuing them. The kangaroo rat grows to a length of twelve inches and has a sandy to dark-brown coat with pure-white underparts and feet.

The fourteen species are most abundant in the Southwest although one is found in the central plains states. Many naturalists consider kangaroo rats to be the most handsome of the rodents; their gentle disposition and clean habits make them excellent pets. In nature they are active only at night, when they gather seeds and other plant parts in their ample cheek pouches and transport the loads to their burrows. Such large quantities of food are stored that fourteen bushels of dried grasses and seeds were found in one burrow, each kind of seed stored neatly by itself. The openings to their underground quarters may be a hole level with the ground or one surrounded by a mound. In very hot or very cold weather they remain hidden in their burrows.

MUSKRAT. This animal is more like a little beaver than a rat; the name comes from the musk glands which give off a sweetish scent. A fullgrown muskrat is larger than any other rat, with a length of twenty-four inches and a weight of three or four pounds. It spends a great deal of its life in the water, being specially adapted for swimming by having webbed hind feet. The dense glossy fur, brownish on the back and lighter beneath, has a soft underfur which gives the muskrat waterproof covering as well as a warm blanket. It is this underfur which makes the muskrat pelt valuable; when processed it is known as Hudson seal. Millions of muskrats are trapped annually for this purpose.

Muskrats are found in practically every state. They are active at all seasons, and at all times of day. They enjoy nibbling on the juicy stems of cattails, pondweed, and arrowhead; muskrats swim under the ice in winter to reach these plants. In addition they eat crayfish, clams, mussels, and salamanders. The home of a muskrat is located in shallow water and is a clumsy structure of branches and sticks, rising as a cone some six or eight feet in diameter and four feet in height. Muskrats often build feeding platforms near their lodges on which they sit and eat their meals. Usually muskrats live alone, but there are records of a dozen or more individuals getting together in a "dormitory" to keep warm during the colder months.

PORCUPINE. Nature has endowed the porcupine with one of the most ingenious devices found among mammals—body armor which is out of the way when not needed but instantly available when the occasion demands it. This large rodent has such faith in its quills that it ignores flight as a means of escape. The animal simply turns its back, erects the sharp spines and swings the short but well armored tail in the face of its adversary. The porcupine is sometimes inaccurately called a hedgehog. The European hedgehog is an insectivor, not a rodent, and thus not even a close relative of our American porcupine.

Anyone who has camped or hiked in the woodlands of the northeastern states, the Great Lakes region, the Rocky Mountains, or the Pacific coast ranges has sooner or later caught a glimpse of this lumbering animal with small head, hunched back, and short legs. The chunky body is covered with thick, brown or black underfur and yellowish or white long guard hairs. Intermingled with these on the head, upper parts of the body, and tail are numerous needle-sharp hollow quills, one to five inches in length. When a porcupine is undisturbed the quills lie close to the body, hidden in the underfur; but when the animal is alarmed the quills are raised to an erect position. The quills come out easily and become imbedded in the face and feet of the attacker. Each quill is armed with tiny barbs which enable the quill to work deeper into the flesh. A hungry carnivor with its mouth and stomach lining pierced by these quills may well die of starvation; if it survives, it will give a wide berth to the next porcupine it meets. The belief that a porcupine can throw or shoot its quills is not founded on fact. However, these quills are so loosely attached that, when the tail is rapidly swung from side to side, they are readily transferred to the attacker.

A full-grown porcupine grows to a length of three feet and may weigh as much as fifteen or twenty pounds. It walks with its heels on the ground, as a bear or man walks. The forefeet have four long sharp claws, the hind-feet five. These make it possible for the porcupine to climb unusually well for its size and shape. Much of its time is spent in trees, either feeding, sleeping, or resting. Porcupines are most common in conifer or aspen-poplar woods. Here they eat all kinds of plant food during the summer, but rely on the inner bark of trees in winter. Thus at this time of year they cause considerable damage by girdling the trees at snowline. Porcupines are very fond of salt and will gnaw tools and other articles which have traces of sweat on them. They also have a strange fondness for bones on which they gnaw, perhaps to sharpen their incisors.

Porcupines do not have definite nests or specially con-structed dens. They "hole in" where they can find a convenient opening in a rock pile or under a rocky ledge. They are hardy animals, active at all seasons and in all kinds of weather. When the going is hard because of deep snow, a porcupine will spend much time stretched out on a tree limb, kept warm by its thick underfur. The young are born singly, in May or June. The quills harden an hour after the young porcupine is born. In captivity porcupines have lived for ten years.

BEAVER. No mammal has played a more significant role in the history of this country than the beaver. It was the search for beaver pelts which sent the white man into the unexplored vastness of the new world. In pioneer days, beaver skins became the medium of exchange for such commodities as tobacco, food, cooking utensils, and rifles. Many American fortunes were built on exploita-tion of this animal. The resulting drain on our beaver population almost caused the extinction of the species. In one twenty-five-year period of the last century the Hudson Bay Company alone delivered 3,000,000 skins to the London market. Fortunately, a decline in trapping plus conservation and protection practices averted total extinction of this interesting animal. Today the beaver is holding its own. It can be found in practically every state, wherever there are streams. Because beaver dams are an excellent means of controlling erosion, these animals have been re-introduced in many regions where they had become extinct. The beaver has long been the symbol of industry, and is justly famed as an architect and engineer. Its accomplishments, and those of other animal home-builders, will be described later.

The beaver wears an overcoat of rich brown with underwear of close fur which keeps the beaver dry and warm. Adults grow to a length of three or four feet and may weigh up to sixty pounds. When a beaver is swimming, the square profile is a reliable identification, setting this animal apart from its aquatic neighbors, the muskrat and otter. The muskrat is smaller and has a less angular profile, that of the otter is distinctly rounded. As might be expected in an animal which can cut down large trees, the incisor teeth of beaver are powerful tools. Trunks felled by beavers show large clean cuts as if made with an axe. Beavers are always found near water, being equipped by nature to lead an amphibious existence. They can hold their breath under water for periods up to fifteen minutes; their webbed hindfeet enable them to swim with ease and speed; their flattened oar-like tail acts as a scull and a rudder.

Beavers are strictly herbivorous, feeding on plants

growing in or near water, especially on the bark of such trees as aspen poplar, willow, alder, and birch. These same trees are cut and stored under water by beavers, to be used as food during the winter. Signs of beaver activity are more frequently seen than the animals themselves. Felled trees, chips, dams, canals, and lodges can be observed along waterways throughout the wooded sections of most of our northern states. Beavers generally stay out of sight during the day and emerge at dusk for their work

A beaver wears an overcoat of rich brown fur, but has a hairless tail which serves as a rudder, a sculling oar, and a fifth leg when the animal is on land.

and play. When alarmed, a beaver will slap the water with its scaly tail, producing a report like a gunshot.

A beaver goes about its work quietly, rarely uttering any sound, being neither quarrelsome, aggressive, nor gregarious. The female has several litters of "kits" a year, with an average of five babies in each litter. The young beaver is born well furred, with eyes open, and in a few hours gets about by itself.

RABBITS, HARES, AND PIKAS

Rabbits and hares are familiar animals in every state; they are known by their long ears and elongated hindlegs. All rabbits and hares chew with a peculiar sidewise motion because their lower jaw is narrower than the upper. Thus when the right molars are together, the lower molars on the left side are inside the upper ones. Rabbits differ from hares in having smaller ears and shorter legs. Young rabbits are born naked, blind, and helpless while young hares are fully furred with eyes open when they greet the outside world.

COTTONTAIL. This common rabbit is recognized by the white underside of the tail, revealed like a powderpuff when the animal bounds away. The eastern cottontail, found in thickets and roadside weed patches as far west as the Rocky Mountains, reaches a length of eighteen inches and a weight of four pounds. Cottontails eat such a variety of vegetable food that it would be easier to list what they don't eat rather than what they do. They become a nuisance in crop and garden areas because of their vegetarian habits. They usually sit hunched up, as inconspicuous as possible, in their resting places during the day, coming forth at sunset to forage until

JACK RABBIT

COTTONTAIL

WINTER

SUMMER

PIKA

SNOWSHOE RABBIT

Rabbits, Hares, and Pika.

dawn. Rabbits furnish more sport for hunters than all other game species combined. In addition, numerous varieties of the European rabbit are raised as pets.

The cottontail constructs no special den or home, being content with hollowing out a bowl-shaped depression in the ground, called a "form," usually hidden by grasses. In winter it may take over an abandoned woodchuck burrow or a vacated fox den. More often the temporary quarters are a simple hideaway under a brush pile. Three to five litters, each of four or five young, arrive in summer. The young are born in a shallow depression in the earth, dug by the mother. She does not stay with her babies except when feeding them. Having little protection, many of the young rabbits die of pneumonia or other disease; others are eaten by snakes, crows, red squirrels, and dogs. The high birth rate, however, keeps the cottontail population far from extinction.

MARSH RABBITS. The eastern cottontail has several relatives in the South and West. In the dense swamps and wet lowlands of the Atlantic coastal plain, from Virginia to Florida, lives the marsh rabbit. It is slightly smaller than the cottontail, with shorter ears; its fur is reddish or blackish brown. Most distinctive difference, however, is the lack of the white underside to the tail. The SWAMP RABBIT of the canebrakes and bottom-lands from Alabama to Texas is the largest of the group, reaching a length of twenty inches and weighing up to six pounds. The fur coat is reddish or black, and the tail has the typical white underside found in the cottontail. On the arid plains and deserts found from Texas to California lives the DESERT COTTONTAIL, very similar to the eastern cottontail in general appearance and size.

VARYING HARE.   This hare, with a length of eighteen or twenty inches, is much larger than the cottontail; it gets its name because it changes its coat with the seasons. In summer the fur is grayish brown, in winter it is pure white. It is also known as the snowshoe rabbit because of its big, hairy-soled feet which keep the hare from breaking through soft snow or slipping on an icy crust. A forest mammal of Canada and Alaska, it has spread into the cooler northeastern and north central states, as well as into the Northwest.

The varying hare is a fleet-footed animal, its powerful hindlegs propelling it in ten-foot leaps at a speed of thirty miles an hour. At high speeds the tracks reveal that the hindfeet strike the ground far in front of the forefeet. In escaping a pursuer, the hare can twist and dodge while in the air and thus is likely to race off in a different direction from its original course. When sitting still it is very well concealed by its protective coloration.

Like the rabbits, the hares have simple homes, often just a "form" in the ground or under the shelter of a log. The young are born, three or four in a litter, wherever the mother happens to be at the moment. The babies are left to themselves during the day; the mother returns at night to nurse them. Few varying hares live to be more than two years old. On moonlit nights these hares get together sitting in silence, occasionally thumping with their hindfeet, or chasing each other playfully. Hares make a network of trails, many well beaten by countless generations; where the trail passes a favorite eating place, such as a few fallen poplars, the ground may be packed hard. Hares likewise enjoy a meal of willows, birches, and maples destructively girdling the tree as do the eastern rabbits and porcupine. In summer they feed on grasses, clover, dandelion, and shoots of raspberry and blackberry.

For the varying hare to change its summer coat for a winter one is not a simple procedure. The gray under-fur remains the same, year round, but in late autumn the long black guard hairs and the shorter yellow and black fur is replaced by new white hairs. The change, which requires ten weeks and is normally complete by the first snowfall, begins on the ears and feet, and continues toward the rest of the body until the animal is all in white except for the black-tipped ears. There are two sets of hair roots, so the winter fur can grow in before the complete shedding of the summer coat; otherwise the animal might freeze to death. In early spring, the winter coat is replaced by a reddish brown one, the process taking place in reverse order, ending with the ears and feet. This change goes by the calendar and not the weather, so that in winters of light snowfall the hare may be very conspicuous, or when it still wears the summer coat and an early snowfall occurs.

JACK RABBIT. This hare is named for its huge jackass-like ears which are proportionally larger than those of any other mammal. In one species the ears are one-third the total body length. They function as sensitive, directional air-scoops to pick up sounds which otherwise would be unnoticed. Jack rabbits rely on speed to escape their enemies; only a greyhound can catch a jack on a straightaway. Slower animals such as the coyote and fox depend on wit rather than speed to catch a rabbit. In short bursts, jack rabbits have been clocked at forty-five miles per hour. The champion high-jumper of all our mammals, these hares can leap fifteen or twenty feet in their "spy leaps"—especially high leaps made almost vertically between many shorter ones in order to watch their enemies.

There are two kinds of jack rabbits. The white-tailed jack, buff colored or gray in summer, changes like the varying hare to a pure white coat in winter. These large hares, weighing up to thirteen pounds, live in the plains states and on the western mountains from the Dakotas to Kansas and westward. The black-tailed jack rabbits live in the more southern plains states from Kansas to Texas, west to California.

Jack rabbits eat grass and foliage, and occasionally raid cultivated crop fields. Large bands sometimes raid clover and alfalfa fields in the irrigated valleys and then retreat to their sagebrush home, leaving considerable damage behind. Fifteen jack rabbits can eat as much as one sheep. Unwise killing of coyotes by the farmers of

Footprints of Some Common Gnawing Animals.

the Southwest has often allowed a great increase in the jack rabbit population with accompanying crop damage. The females have two to four litters a year, with at least three young in each litter; hence the rabbit population grows rapidly unless kept in check by carnivors.

Jack rabbits like open areas with plenty of room for a speedy getaway; they are most active at night. During the mating season males can often be seen standing erect and sparring with other males in boxing matches. They box with their forepaws, and at times deliver effective blows even with their hindlimbs.

PIKA. The pika, or cony, is a small gray or buff animal only seven or eight inches long resembling a guinea pig; the tail is so short that for all practical purposes it is non-existent. It is a solitary and busy little animal, emerging from its well hidden home amid rocks and boulders to feed on grasses and alpine plants which grow in its mountain environment in the Rockies and the ranges of the Pacific coast states. The pika is a thrifty individual, gathering and drying piles of grass in "haystacks" near its home, to be a handy store of food during the long winter. Unlike its relatives the rabbits, it is active by day, moving noiselessly over the rocks since its tiny feet are furred on the soles. Often a pika will take a sun bath on a rocky slope, absorbing gratefully the warmth of the brief summer. It has a peculiar bleating call, and also an explosive "kaa-a-a-ck" which sets the mountain echoes ringing.

*

It is fitting that we should bring to a close our survey of the rodents and their relatives with the tiny pika of the

West. Our introduction to the gnawing animals was the common squirrels which have become accustomed to living near humans in the comfort of our eastern woodlands and in a not too-exacting climate. The rugged pika on the other hand has chosen to live a solitary existence in a rigorous habitat shunned by man, at elevations of 13,000 feet above sea level. In its inhospitable world, when winter sets in, the pika still remains, neither migrating nor hibernating. Between the two extremes of animal life occurs a wide variety of rodent and rabbit-like animals; some active by day others by night; some living in the water, others going their entire lives without water; some becoming home-bodies with carefully constructed living quarters, others remaining transients amid their more comfortably housed neighbors; some aggressively preying on other animals, others content to browse their lives away. There is no doubt that the gnawing animals make up a diversified and interesting group of mammals, well adapted to a great variety of habitats. They are fascinating subjects for mammal-watching.

It is a memorable experience to come face-to-face with a stately Virginia deer in the full glory of its antlers.

CHAPTER THREE

THE HOOFED MAMMALS

A stately buck deer in the full glory of his antlers is poised alert and ready to bound away into the shadows of the forest. This is truly a memorable sight; in fact, a meeting with any of our native hoofed animals is a high spot on a camping trip or vacation. Although in number of species they do not comprise a large portion of our wild life, they make up for this in beauty and appeal to both naturalist and sportsman.

The hoof, an unusual adaptation of the foot, gives the group its most easily recognized feature. But hoofed animals have specialized also in adaptation of the teeth for a herbivorous diet. Incisor and canine teeth are absent or inconspicuous, but the premolars and molars are effective grinding surfaces for mashing foliage and grass into digestible form. The group is also distinctive in having bony outgrowths of the skull in the form of horns or antlers.

A hoofed animal stands on its toes, in the same manner as a toe-dancer. This puts a great strain on the tip of the digits, as well as on the long slender limbs. As a special protection for the digit bones and soft part of the toe, the toenail has developed into a hoof. Rodents, as we have seen, have claws on the tips of their digits; a claw is a toenail with two horny scale-like plates converging into a point, with a leathery cushion or pad on the underside. A hoof consists of the same parts as a claw, but the upper horny plate is not pointed and the under plate is reduced to a small remnant. The cushion forms a tough pad or "frog" capable of bearing the weight of the animal, and of standing the wear and tear of constant contact with the ground. In a hoofed animal the "frog" functions like the rubber heel of a shoe. The lower plate wears away at a faster rate than the upper, leaving the latter with a sharp edge. This gives many hoofed mammals a sure-footed grip on the ground. In the mountain goat, each hoof has a concave sole which functions like a suction cup. The two hoofs on each foot give an added advantage; the cleft between the two toes opens to the front, so that when descending a steep cliff the weight of the animal spreads this cleft apart and gives a secure purchase on steep uneven ground.

THE DEER FAMILY

Members of the deer family have solid antlers of bone which are outgrowths of the skull, shed and renewed annually. They are the special adornment of the males in the deer family, except in the caribou and reindeer where both males and females have antlers. At first the antler is covered with hairy skin; in this condition the deer is said to be "in velvet." As the antler grows it remains covered with skin; when mature the skin dries and shreds off. The buck usually hastens this process by rubbing his new antlers against trees and stones. This leaves the antlers polished bone, often with extremely sharp tines. When the antlers are shed, skin grows over the wound. The next season when other antlers develop they usually have more branches and prongs than those of the preceding year. In addition to the two hoofs on each foot, representing the third and fourth toes, remains of the second and fifth toes occur as "dewclaws" which do not touch the ground. A deer's skull reveals the absence of upper incisors and all the canine teeth. There is a full complement of twelve premolars and molars in each jaw.

WHITETAIL.   It is reassuring to find, in the face of the diminishing numbers of many of our large game animals, one species which is not only holding its own but even becoming more numerous than it ever has been. The whitetail, or Virginia deer, has prospered so well in the eastern states that its population today is over 5,000,-000. Deer, like beaver, have played an important role in the early history of our country. The Indians and later the colonists relied upon deer for venison before other kinds of meat were available, for buckskin as material for their clothes, for thread, and for implements made of bone. Thus deer rapidly became scarcer as more and more white men invaded the land. But unexpectedly living conditions favorable to an increasing deer population came about as a by-product of the lumbering industry. The thousands of acres of cut-over timber-land provided second-growth vegetation ideal for deer browsing. Added to this, conservation and wise hunting practices were put into effect in ample time to guarantee the survival of a large whitetail population.

The whitetail, found throughout the United States east of the Rocky Mountains, is familiar to everyone who has spent any time in the out-of-doors. It averages three feet in height at the shoulders, is about five or six feet in length, and weighs from fifty to three hundred pounds. The larger individuals are found in the northern part of the country, especially in New England and New York. Farther south the deer become smaller so that there a one-hundred-pound buck is the usual size. Tiniest of all are the dwarf Key deer found on Big Pine Key, Florida. The light-weight summer coat of the whitetail is of short fine hairs distinctly reddish in color. In autumn this is replaced by a grayish brown coat of coarse bristle-like hairs which provide a warm covering for the coming winter. The whitetail gets its name from the bushy tail, brown above but pure white beneath; when alarmed, the deer erects its tail so that the white color flashes a conspicuous signal as the animal bounds away. Deer have an uncanny sense of smell and hearing, relying on these rather than eyesight to escape their enemies.

Antlers first appear on the bucks in spring as small swellings in front of the ears; these grow in size until by August they are fully formed. A year-old buck has only a few prongs, but each successive season the new antlers are larger and have more branches, until a maximum number of twelve "points" is reached as the usual number at five years of age. For the next three years, after every shedding, the antlers get heavier but the number of branches remains the same. As the buck grows older

FEBRUARY

MARCH

MAY

JUNE

AUGUST

SEPTEMBER

Antler Growth in a Mule Deer.

the antlers become less massive and have fewer branches; a twelve-year-old may actually have simple antlers. A record set of antlers on a Canadian whitetail had a spread of thirty-three inches and a length of thirty inches, with the unusual number of twenty-six "points." Deer reach their prime at six years, and are old at ten. Those lucky enough to escape disease and such enemies as coyote, wolf, and hunter may live for fifteen years. As with most wild animals, few die of old age.

Deer feed on a variety of plant growth depending upon the season and what is available. During spring and summer, grass and weeds make up most of their menu. They also browse on foliage of maples, willows, oaks, sassafras, and dogwood; at some seasons they eat ferns, water lilies, and mushrooms. At times deer have been known to catch and eat fish. In fall they gorge themselves on acorns and apples when they can find these delicacies. Deer also have their dislikes. They show a strange antagonism to snakes, jumping on them and stamping them to death. During the annoying season of flies and mosquitoes, deer seek relief in the waters of streams and ponds where they swim very well.

The fawns, usually twins, are born in May or June, being carefully hidden on the ground in a thicket. A fawn is marked with white spots; when it flattens itself motionless against the earth the camouflage is so effective that it resembles a log or stone mottled with sunlight and shadow. For several weeks the fawn remains quietly in one spot, nursed by the mother who returns several times a day for this purpose. As winter approaches, deer become more gregarious, feeding together in a sheltered area known to hunters as a "yard." Since their hoofs are too small to paw through the snow and thus uncover vegetation, they are forced to feed on buds, twigs, and bark of deciduous trees, or, as a last resort, on the foliage of fir balsam or juniper.

MULE DEER. In the Rocky Mountains and farther west to the Pacific coast, the whitetail is replaced by the mule deer, so named because of the large ears, usually twisted forward to catch the slightest sound. These are the friendly deer which delight tourists in our western national parks. They are not as gracefully proportioned as the whitetails, having a heavier body and more stocky legs. Mule deer travel ordinarily by leaps and bounds; in fact, they are called "jumping deer" in some parts of Canada. This gait, with horizontal leaps of fifteen or twenty feet can carry the mule deer over the ground at speeds up to thirty-five miles per hour. The brownish, rather than reddish, summer coat is replaced in winter by a grayish one. The rounded white tail with black tip is very different from that of the whitetail. Mule deer are usually less than three feet high at the shoulders, and rarely weigh more than two hundred pounds. The antlers, which may have branched tines, have a maximum spread of thirty-six inches, and length of thirty-three inches; a record set had ten "points."

Mule deer often have two different ranges, within fifty or a hundred miles of each other. The fawns are born when the mothers reach the summer range, which often is among the aspen and pine forests at altitudes of 7000 to 8000 feet. The fawns of the mule deer, usually twins, are born in June or July. Each fawn weighs about six pounds at birth. With the coming of winter the bands of mule deer migrate to the lower valleys where they feed on fir and juniper. Grass and juicy weeds are preferred as food; other items on the mule-deer menu include sagebrush, berry bushes, aspens, willows, mistletoe, and mushrooms. Their enemies are the coyote and cougar; bear are too clumsy to catch adults, but take advantage of the unprotected fawns.

BLACKTAIL. The Columbia black-tailed deer, a close relative of the mule deer, is found in the redwood and fir forests of the Pacific coast. This deer is smaller than its relatives, and has a darker coat; its most distinctive feature is the tail which is dark brown or black above and white underneath. Blacktails stand about three feet high at the shoulders, weigh up to one hundred and fifty pounds. The gait of this forest-dwelling species is halfway between the run of the whitetail and the gallop of the mule deer. There is little grass in its native habitat; thus the blacktail is a browsing animal, relying on foliage and buds of woody plants. In spring it looks eagerly for the first tender shoots of skunk cabbage and other succulent plants; in fall it fattens on acorns.

ELK. This name was given by the colonists to the magnificent American deer known as Wapiti by the Shawnee Indians. Elk are large animals, unique in their mane and huge spreading antlers. Four to five feet high at the shoulders, elk may weigh as much as six hundred pounds. The summer coat is a tawny brown, the long-haired winter coat is grayish; at all seasons elk have a conspicuous whitish rump patch.

Elk formerly ranged over the northern two-thirds of

the United States, from the Berkshires of New England to the Pacific coast. Almost all had been slaughtered by 1900, but extinction was prevented by prompt protective measures. By 1943 the population had increased to 200,-000 and ten years later a wild-life census indicated 300,-000. Elk are mainly mountain dwellers, with local seasonal migrations from the low protected valleys where they winter to the exposed higher slopes in summer. One of the best known elk sanctuaries is the Elk Refuge of the Biological Survey in Jackson Hole, Wyoming, where the Yellowstone herd spends the winter.

Bull elk become vocal during the mating season with loud bugling which sets the mountain echoes ringing. Each bull ambitiously tries to collect as many does as possible; sometimes his harem may number sixty females. The fully antlered and restless young bucks try to steal the harems of older bulls; many a fierce battle is waged, the contenders charging each other head on with clashing antlers. The loser, if not fatally hurt, wanders away to seek another easier battle. Each cow has a single calf, born the following May or June; it weighs about thirty pounds. The life span of an elk is about ten years, although in captivity individuals have lived to be twenty-five years old.

Elk are herd animals throughout the year, both sexes and all age groups joining forces during the winter. The calves when a few days old are able to follow the mothers on the trek to summer feeding grounds. Here in protected valleys elk find some shelter, but food is often scarce for the grasses lie buried beneath snow; thus they must browse on the less nutritious foliage of Douglas fir and juniper. The critical factor in the survival of elk is availability of winter feeding grounds, which are increasingly rare in mountainous country where the valleys have been utilized for agriculture and cattle raising.

Elk have keen hearing and a good sense of smell, which aids them in the constant battle for survival against their enemies—the cougar, wolf, and coyote. The principal stronghold of elk today is in Yellowstone National Park, but they are also found in Montana and Idaho. A large dark-colored variety, the Roosevelt elk, lives in the humid redwood and fir belt of Oregon and Washington. A dwindling branch of the family includes the smaller and paler Tule elk, found only in a few counties of California.

MOOSE. The deer family includes some of the most graceful animals in the world. But it also boasts one of the most ungainly and oddly proportioned of all American mammals: the moose. This personification of calm, deliberate strength has a huge humped body with thick neck, ponderous head, stilt-like legs; the drooping muzzle with pendulous lower lip is out of proportion to the rest of the head. As if to compensate for these uncouth features, nature has endowed the moose with the most splendid set of antlers to be found on any animal. Broad and sweeping, with shovel-like flattened branches, these antlers attain a spread of fifty-eight inches. A fullgrown bull moose measures seven feet high at the shoulders and may weigh up to a ton. Standing erect on its hindlegs it can browse on foliage ten feet above the ground. A peculiar "bell" of hair and skin hangs from the throat.

Moose are rugged, cold-weather animals which thrive in Canada; small numbers range southward into the cool conifer forests of northern New England and New York,

Minnesota, and the northern Rocky Mountains. Being prized as a game animal, it is threatened with extinction; but the diminishing numbers in the East have been offset by protection afforded in some of the western national parks. Today the moose population is estimated at 13,000 with prospects of a slow but steady increase in the numbers of this unusual mammal.

Moose travel very little, spending most of their lives in one area, preferably near a pond or swamp where they browse leisurely and spend hours placidly chewing their cud. In winter they are kept warm by inch-thick fur; at this season they gather in small bands in secluded swamps. They like to wade in shallow ponds where they graze on underwater vegetation. At times they may submerge completely in order to reach tasty aquatic plants; they have a special liking for pond lilies. They are very much at home in the water, and are good swimmers. Moose browse on birch, maple, and willow during the summer, and on fir and low-growing yew in the winter.

A bull has only one mate at a time. Both bulls and cows call during the mating season, which is in September and October. The bull call is a hoarse bellow, that of the cow is similar to the mooing of a domesticated cow. The twin calves are born in May or June; each calf has a uniformly colored reddish brown coat, and a black muzzle. It weighs about twenty pounds, and can walk a few hours after its birth. The awkward youngsters remain with their mothers for a year; they do not mature until twelve years old. Except during mating season, the moose are not dangerous and rarely attack man. They are very wary, and usually disappear before one can get very close to them. Their natural enemy is the wolf; and even this carnivor waits to pick off an old or crippled moose, or a defenseless calf.

THE PRONGHORN FAMILY

This unique North American family includes but a single species, the pronghorn antelope. Both sexes bear horns which consist of a permanent bony core with a horny sheath which is shed annually. They have no upper front teeth (incisors and canines) and no lower canines; premolars are present as in the deer family. Each limb has only two hoofs; there are no dewclaws since the other two toes have no visible remnents.

PRONGHORN ANTELOPE. This graceful creature of the wide open spaces, with muscular limbs and sharp hoofs, can travel in fifteen-foot leaps at speeds up to sixty miles per hour. Twenty miles an hour is a comfortable loafing gait. Smaller than a whitetail deer, a pronghorn stands under three feet high at the shoulders and weighs about one hundred pounds. The warm tan color of the upper parts of the body changes to a grayish brown in winter; two white bands mark the throat. The black horns grow larger after each shedding until at the fifth year those of the bucks reach their maximum length of fifteen inches.

When the pronghorn is alarmed, the large white rump patch becomes especially noticeable as the hairs of this area stand erect. This signal warns all other pronghorns in the neighborhood of danger. Soon the landscape is dotted with flashing specks of white where a moment before no animal could be seen. A strange trait is the pronghorn's impulse to outrun anything that moves, even an automobile. In a final burst of speed it will dash in front of its rival and then slow down, satisfied with the demonstration of its prowess.

In summer pronghorns feed on grass and weeds, and also raid alfalfa fields in the irrigated valleys. During winter they subsist on sagebrush and other available shrubs. In some parts of their range, pronghorns migrate in winter from the mountains, where deep snow covers their food supply, to the lowlands. Chief enemies are coyotes and wolves, but these carnivors are not fast enough to catch a healthy fullgrown pronghorn. However coyotes have learned the trick of pursuing their fleet-footed prey in relays, one coyote taking up the chase when another tires and drops out. When flight is of no use, a pronghorn will fight vigorously, using its sharp hoofs as weapons.

A family group consists of a buck and a small group of does. The fawns, usually twins, are born in May or June, wherever the mother happens to be at the time. In a few days each fawn can take care of itself and runs alongside the mother. Pronghorn bucks are not as belligerent as bucks of other kinds of hoofed animals, and serious fights between rivals even during the mating season are rare. Both bucks and does are extremely nervous by nature, and bolt at the slightest movement on the part of an observer.

The struggle of the pronghorn against civilization repeats the story of many other hoofed animals. In colonial days they roamed the plains in large herds, estimated to contain at least 50,000,000 individuals. By 1908 agriculture and cattle raising had eliminated their natural feeding grounds; these factors and hunting had reduced the millions to 19,000. The inauguration of protective controls saved the species, so that the 1945 population reached 250,000 and by 1953 had increased to 340,000. The natural range of the pronghorn extends from the northern Rocky Mountains to the arid Southwest. Many suitable areas in Colorado, Montana, Wyoming, the Dakotas, and New Mexico have been restocked. As a result today we are assured of the survival of this graceful, fleet-footed native American.

THE CATTLE FAMILY

In the cattle family both sexes have permanent horns. The horn of a cow or a buffalo is a sheath covering the permanent bony core. The horn is not shed but grows in size by the addition of new material from the layer of living tissue between it and the bony core. The teeth and stomach of the cattle family are well adapted for securing and digesting plant food. Domesticated members include all the familiar cattle; our wild species are the buffalo, bighorn sheep, and mountain goat.

BUFFALO. No other American animal brings to mind such vivid pictures of the old Wild West, of frontiersmen like Daniel Boone and Buffalo Bill Cody, of wagon trains crawling amid herds of thundering buffalo, of construction gangs subsisting on buffalo meat while building the first transcontinental railroad. The buffalo, in fact, is the symbol of a vanishing wild life which was America.

The American buffalo, or bison, has a high shoulder hump, massive head, and a shaggy fur coat which are familiar in pictures to every schoolchild. The winter coat is a light yellowish brown, the summer attire a darker brown especially on the head and legs. The horns seem small compared to the rest of the huge animal; those of the females are more slender and curved than those of the males. The largest buffalo skull on record had twenty-two inch horns with a spread of thirty-five inches. The other end of the animal terminates in a ridiculously small tufted tail. Buffalo bulls are much larger than the cows, with a length of eleven feet (cows rarely exceed seven feet), standing five feet high at the shoulders and weighing a ton or more. As might be expected from their relatively small eyes, buffalo have poor eyesight but their senses of hearing and smell are highly developed. Their voice can be a terror-inspiring bellow.

Buffalo are gregarious animals. The smallest group is the family, dominated by an old cow and including several generations of her calves. A herd is formed by many families joining forces. The bulls, usually anti-social, join the herds at times, particularly in winter. During the

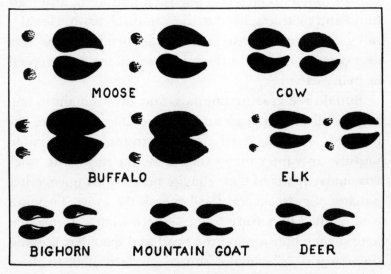

Footprints of Some Common Hoofed Animals.

mating season, in July and August, the bulls become dangerous. Their rivalry results in battles of titans as they charge head-on like a pair of locomotives. The terrific impact of ton against ton is borne by the skulls of the contestants, since the horns are too small to be of much value. It is remarkable that so few bulls are injured in these encounters. After a few rounds, the loser generally leaves the scene, undoubtedly with a splitting headache! Ordinarily buffalo are timid animals, but they are sufficiently unpredictable to make it wise to watch them warily.

Buffalo calves, born singly, are a bright tawny brown at birth. They arrive in May and each remains with its mother until the next calf arrives. A few days after birth the calf is strong enough to follow the mother in her travels. Buffalo become mature at eight years, and are old at fourteen. In exceptional cases buffalo have been known to live to be forty; one such patriarch, although blind and toothless, lived to die a natural death. Healthy full grown buffalo have few natural enemies, but wolves and cougars eliminate the cripples and the sick, as well as many calves.

Buffalo are grazing animals, and thus remain in one area until all the grass and other edible plants are exhausted. Then the herd moves on to the next available pasture. In winter they sweep aside the snow with sidewise movements of their shaggy heads, thus uncovering patches of grass several feet beneath the snow. They are well clothed by nature to face severe winter storms, the long shaggy hair around the head and shoulders keeping them warm. The major source of discomfort to these giants is the great number of flies, mosquitoes, and other insects which infest them in summer. Buffalo roll in the dust and mud to get rid of the irritating pests. Buffalo wallows were common landmarks of the prairies, deep troughs in which the huge animals rolled and kicked while raising a cloud of dust or a shower of mud. Buffalo have friends among the magpies and cowbirds which perch on their backs and pick off the insects.

The story of the buffalo almost ended with the tragic extinction of this great mammal. Early American explorers found buffalo in western Pennsylvania, along the headwaters of the Potomac River, in Kentucky, Georgia, and even northern Florida. But buffalo reached their greatest development in the central states where the natural grasslands could support a tremendous population of grazing animals. Only on the Pacific coast and in the desert Southwest were they absent. A scientific guess as to their numbers places the population at some 60,000,-000 when the white man came to this country. It has been said that civilized man never witnessed a greater assemblage of animals anywhere on earth.

Yet these seemingly limitless numbers were practically wiped out in the tidal wave of advancing civilization. By 1820 not one buffalo remained east of the Mississippi River. At the turn of the century, of the countless millions of a hundred years before, only 541 were left in the entire United States! Public opinion was aroused at this critical point and protection of this vanishing American mammal became a public responsibility. Herds were reestablished in many portions of the original habitat. Today the buffalo population in the United States has mounted to 6,000 and is steadily growing. A large herd of 12,000 is thriving in Wood Buffalo Park, Canada. Our own herds can be seen in Yellowstone National Park, in Wind Cave National Park of the South Dakota Black Hills, and in the National Bison Range of western Montana.

BIGHORN.   The sure-footed bighorn or Rocky Mountain sheep are the wild sheep of North America. Their fur coat, unlike that of domesticated sheep, is not wooly, but hairy like the coat of a deer. The color varies from light brown to brownish black, depending upon the geographic home of the animal. Bighorn are the mountain climbers of the animal world, found among the crags and cliffs; but at times they descend into the desert lowlands or plains to feed. Bighorn can outclimb all their four-footed enemies, but cannot escape the rifle bullets of man. Over-hunting as well as loss of feeding range to livestock brought the race perilously near extinction. Legal hunting of these unique mammals, except in a few localities in Wyoming and Idaho, was abolished years ago. Originally they could be found throughout the mountainous areas of western United States, from Canada to the Mexican border.

The horns of the rams are massive and recurved, those of the ewes and kids are smaller and only slightly curved. Unfortunately for the species, the huge yet graceful horns, sometimes growing in a full circle, are greatly prized hunting trophies. Record horns measure fifty inches along the outside curve, and have a spread of thirty inches. A bighorn ram may weigh two hundred pounds or more, and stand three feet high at the shoulders. Their food consists of grass, alpine plants, and any available vegetation. Between periods of eating they lie in some craggy hollow and chew their cud.

In October and November the rams become restless, jealous of each other, and stage butting contests which are the most spectacular performances of our wild life. This has been well described by Cahalane in his "Mammals of North America."

"Sometimes these duels seem to follow a definite routine with certain rules for position and movements. Two rams may open action by standing side by side, but facing in opposite directions. With ferocious grunts and snorts, they strike sideways and upwards at each other with a sharp front hoof. For a few minutes, they tell each other off in this manner. Then they each walk away for about twenty feet. Suddenly, as though at a signal, they turn, rear simultaneously, and charge. Each ram is nearly upright and rushing forward on stiffened hind legs. Without pausing they drop to all fours, crouch, and the two heads crash together. The terrific crack of the heavy, hollow horns can be heard a mile away. The collision causes a ripple or "shock-wave" to roll the entire length of each muscular body. For a few moments the impact dazes the rams. Then they back away and crash again. The battle may be over quickly, or it may last for a couple of hours. It usually ends with both warriors on their feet. They may even walk away, side by side, in an amiable manner .   .   .   .   Sometimes a number of rowdies will jump into a free-for-all. This may become a most exciting battle and continue until the last two contestants are exhausted. .   .   .   Sideswipes with wicked hoofs cut deep bloody gashes, nosebleeds are common, horn tips splintered and sometimes entire horns are broken off short. These will never be replaced. Some rams push their opponents over cliffs. Others are killed

The mountain goat is a shaggy white-coated mountaineer closely
related to the European chamois.

in combat by fractured skulls. By the end of the two-month mating season, many bighorn rams are battered, bruised, and limping."*

The lambs are born, usually singly, in March or April, on a protected ledge or at the foot of a cliff. The ewe stands guard whenever she does not need to eat, during the first weeks of the lamb's life; for the eagle is always on watch for such a toothsome morsel as an unprotected lamb. Soon the lambs can join their mothers and become a part of the band of forty or fifty which grazes along the mountain cliffs. Bighorn sheep live to be seven or eight years old; then their teeth wear out and death soon follows. In captivity they have lived for twenty years.

MOUNTAIN GOAT. This white-coated mountaineer is fortunate in one respect. Few animals or man envy it the cold, windswept slopes above timber-line which are its home. Hence it is left severely alone. So little has this strange hoofed mammal been affected by man and his civilization that it is thought to be about as numerous today as ever. Mountain goats are found in the Rocky Mountains of Montana and Idaho, and in the Cascade Mountains of Washington. This species is actually an antelope, not a true goat, and is closely related to the European chamois.

Living under Arctic conditions much of the year, the mountain goat must be thankful for its warm fur coat of long shaggy hair with an undercoat of fine wool. It is a slightly hunchbacked chunky animal set on short legs, with small backward-curving horns and a beard which gives it the appearance of a quizzical old man. Even

---

* Victor H. Cahalane, *Mammals of North America*, p. 94. Copyright 1947 by The Macmillan Company, and used with their permission.

though only three feet high at the shoulders and five feet in length, it weighs a surprising two hundred to two hundred fifty pounds. Its gait is stiff-legged and deliberate, and its climbing feats are phenomenal; it moves fearlessly with sure-footed ease among its world of sheer cliffs and dizzy heights. For food it relies on the alpine plants, especially grasses, which grow sparsely in its mountain home; even in winter it finds sufficient food to keep alive, on slopes swept bare by winter winds. Ordinarily peace-loving, when attacked by a bear or wolf on one of its trips to the lower wooded slopes, it fights pugnaciously and uses its dagger-like though short horns with telling effect.

Our native hoofed animals were mercilessly slaughtered in our early national growth. As a result they have disappeared from large portions of their original range. But our national parks and monuments have become game refuges where many of the vanishing mammals have found acceptable homes. A large population of moose, elk, mule deer, bighorn sheep, and mountain goats inhabit Glacier National Park. A famous large herd of elk, as well as numerous moose and bighorn sheep, have found sanctuary in Grand Teton National Park. Bighorn and elk are also at home in Rocky Mountain Park. By far our largest "game preserve" is Yellowstone National Park. Here we can see mule deer, elk, antelope, buffalo, and bighorn sheep. We can be thankful that our government has created these national parks where we can see every kind of hoofed animal, living under natural conditions and protected from thoughtless killing and possible extinction.

The face of a gray fox has an expression which suggests the crafti-
ness for which foxes are well known.

CHAPTER FOUR

THE CARNIVORS

Most people believe carnivors are the villains of the animal world, killing ruthlessly whenever they have a chance. When we see a fox pouncing on a rabbit, or a mountain lion overpowering a deer, sympathy is likely to be with the rabbit or the deer. For many years our conservation program was influenced by this view, so that many of our large carnivors were hunted almost to extinction even though their flesh and fur were of little value.

Herbivorous animals are mild-mannered creatures, since it does not require an aggressive nature to get a meal of seeds, fruits, and foliage. On the other hand a carnivor must be strong and wily if it is to capture its meal. The biologist has long realized that carnivors are a necessary part of a well balanced nature. Carnivors do not kill for the pleasure of it but to get their food; for all animals must eat. A carnivor catching and eating its prey is obeying as natural a law as a herbivor browsing on the foliage of a tree.

There is another broader aspect to the story of hunter and hunted. Rodents and hoofed animals if allowed to increase unchecked would reach overwhelming numbers. In their need for food, they might devour so much of the natural vegetation and planted crops that both man and his cattle would suffer for lack of sufficient food for themselves. The flesh-eating mammals can therefore be considered our allies in keeping the gnawing mammals and other herbivors in balance with the rest of our wild life. In addition to keeping the numbers of herbivors within bounds, the carnivors provide a check also on too great increase of their own kind.

Our native carnivors have been the most persecuted of all mammals largely because of lack of understanding of this function in nature. Being meat-eaters they do become destructive to livestock and poultry once they have learned how easy it is to feed on these unwary animals. But the number of domesticated animals killed on these raids is few compared to the enormous quantity of rodents and rabbits which are their natural food. Understanding this relation between the various animals, we can see how easy it is for man to upset the delicate balance of nature by thoughtlessly removing one species from its natural habitat.

Carnivors are adapted in a number of ways for catching their prey and subsisting on fresh meat. They have soft-padded feet on which they can make a noiseless approach. They have long sharp claws with which to grasp and kill their prey. They have effective weapons in the form of sharp canine teeth, and shearing cheek teeth for eating meat. They have well-developed senses, with keen eyes specially suited for seeing in the dark. They have powerful muscles in their limbs and shoulders, a necessity for fighters. And last but not least they have highly developed brains making possible an intelligence which enables them to outwit other wild animals, and often man himself.

Some carnivors are less particular about their food than others. These will eat carrion, and so are valuable scav-

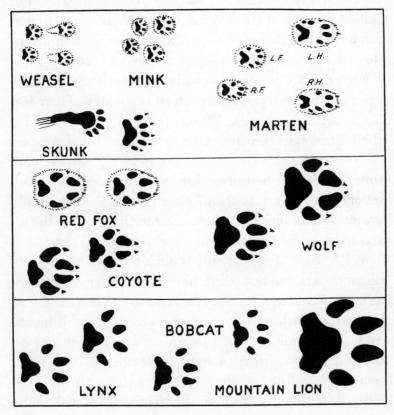

Footprints of Carnivors.

engers. Others eat large amounts of plant food, when fresh meat is not available; these are the omnivors such as the raccoon and bears. The smallest carnivors are in the weasel family. The largest and most formidable are found in the dog and cat families; some of these have become very rare and need protection if they are not to be added to the growing list of vanishing mammals.

THE WEASEL FAMILY

This is the largest family of the carnivors; in it, even though many are small in size, we find some of the most skilled hunters of the animal world. Most of the weasel family are well-armed with dagger-like teeth and endowed with highly developed brains and sense organs. They are able to move quickly and stealthily over the ground, in the trees, and even in the water. Their feet have five clawed toes. Many species are notorious for their scent glands, which give them an unusual weapon of defense; for this reason, the group as a whole is sometimes known as the musk-bearers. All species have a full set of twelve incisor and four canine teeth. Weasels, mink, skunk, and badger have thirty-four teeth; otter has thirty-six; marten, fisher, and wolverine have thirty-eight.

WEASEL.   There are thirty-six kinds of weasel, widely distributed throughout the United States. Variously known as stoat, ferret, and ermine, the weasels can be recognized by their dachshund-like bodies, short legs, small heads, and long supple necks. The underfur is soft and close, the outer fur consists of hard glistening hairs. Weasels which live in the northern states change their fur coats with the seasons. In summer the coat is brown with white underparts; in winter it is all white except for the black tip of the tail. The white coat is of obvious protection when snow is on the ground. The least weasel is our smallest carnivor, being only eight or nine inches in length and weighing only a few ounces. It can be found from Pennsylvania and Ohio westward to Montana. The

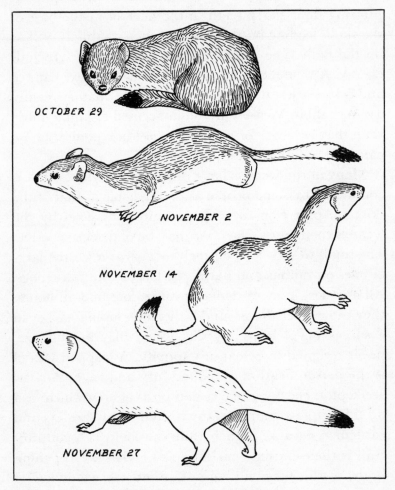

OCTOBER 29

NOVEMBER 2

NOVEMBER 14

NOVEMBER 27

Molting Stages of the Weasel.

short-tailed weasel is common in northeastern United States, and west to the Great Lakes; it is found also in the far West. This slim animal, the size of a chipmunk, weighs three to five ounces. The long-tailed weasel, which is the size of a gray squirrel, is found in every state. When white, its pelt is the most valuable of that of all the weasels.

Weasels are bloodthirsty animals which strike quickly, burying their sharp teeth in the neck or at the base of the skull, feeding on the blood of their victim as well as on the flesh. The supple body is a bundle of ferocious energy. A weasel can move quicker than the eye can see and is so fearless it will sink its teeth in a man as readily as in a rabbit. Weasels are often accused of killing more than they can eat, for a single weasel in a poultry house can destroy fifty chickens in a night.

Many of the weasels have musk glands whose scent is considered by some people as disagreeable as that of the skunk. Apart from use in recognition of sexes by the weasels themselves, the odor may be of defensive value. The small weasels feed on such rodents as mice, the larger ones on rabbits and hares, the largest on prairie dogs. All are alert hunters, active at all seasons and all hours; they move over the ground either in a loping gait or in a succession of leaps. By disposition they are fighters, never resigned to defeat or captivity. A trapped weasel is the personification of baffled fury and rage. Weasels are kept in check by snakes and birds of prey which feed on the helpless young; many are killed by farmers and cattlemen because of their raids on poultry. A contrary trait is their extreme curiosity as to what is happening in the world; they will bark at an intruder yet follow to see what he is doing.

A weasel often appropriates a mouse nest and uses mouse fur to line it for its own comfort. The short-tailed weasel lives along field borders and in open woods, using a hollow under a log or a small cave in the rocks as a den. One to twelve young are born in a litter, usually in spring. Young of the short-tailed weasel weigh only one-fourteenth of an ounce at birth. The babies are pink, toothless, and blind. Soon they can see and follow their mother around, learning to capture insects, small snakes, frogs, and lizards. When full-grown they graduate to a diet of mice, shrews, moles, and small squirrels. They are continually hungry, eating their weight in meat every forty-eight hours.

In the northern states, and at high altitudes, the weasel puts on its royal white ermine coat at the approach of winter. Each brown hair is replaced by a white one so gradually that, while the change takes place, the weasel may have a pepper-and-salt appearance. Sometimes the change does not coincide with the season, and a brown weasel may be conspicuous against the snowbanks of an early snowfall. Other cases are recorded where the white coat remained on the weasel until July. From such instances, biologists reason that the change in color must be the result of heredity rather than caused by a change in the environment. Weasel pelts have a durable soft fur. An individual pelt does not bring a very high price, but it takes a great many to make a fur coat. Ermine has traditionally been the mark of distinction of royalty.

MINK. The beautiful fur coat worn by this member of the weasel family is well known as one of the most costly items of wearing apparel. Thus the unfortunate mink is trapped more extensively than it otherwise would be. The

The mink is an aggressive hunter with a long sinuous body.

mink's fur is a warm russet or chocolate brown, which does not change to white in winter. Mink was the first native furbearer to be "domesticated," and mink farms are today a source of much of the fur used in the trade. Most of the wild mink skins come from Louisiana.

A fullgrown mink is two feet long but weighs only a few pounds. Like its weasel relatives it has short legs and a lithe, sinuous body. It is an aggressive hunter, moving quickly to capture a luckless rabbit or chipmunk. It walks in a slow, lumbering fashion with its back arched, but when necessary it can travel fast and gracefully in long leaps. The favorite hunting grounds of mink are near marshes, streams, and lakes where they capture crayfish, fish, and other aquatic animals. A favorite dish is muskrat, which is pursued into its lodge. A mink will tear open the muskrat house in its search for inhabitants, especially if it thinks young muskrats are in hiding. To add insult to injury, the mink may move in and occupy the home of its victims. Mink do not eat as wastefully as weasels, instead they carry home any surplus meat and store it for future use. Mink have partially webbed hindfeet, and swim and dive gracefully.

Four to eight young are born in a litter, often in a den under the roots of a tree, near a stream bank. The young mink are born blind, the eyes not opening for five weeks. Mother and father are good parents, taking care of the babies and bringing food until they learn to catch their own. In late summer the family group breaks up, with individuals leading a solitary existence during the winter, each having its own hunting territory. Mink are often playful, coasting down mud slides and snowbanks as otter do. Their enemies are the larger carnivors, especially lynx, bobcat, and fox. With typical weasel fury, a mink spits, snarls, hisses, and barks when cornered.

MARTEN. While most of the weasel tribe are content to stay on the ground, this bundle of energy likes to travel in the tree-tops, where it is likely to find its favorite prey, the red squirrel. A golden-brown animal, a little larger than a housecat, the marten has a long lithe body, small head, short legs, and bushy tail; its usual weight is about two or three pounds. Although resembling the mink, the marten has buff-colored patches on the throat and chest and is larger, with more conspicuous ears and a bushier tail. The fisher is of slightly greater size and has darker fur and shorter ears. Its valuable fur, known as sable, is noted for its durability and beauty.

Martens are rugged forest animals, rarely seen by the average naturalist. They roam the conifer forests of northern New England and New York, in the West they can be found in the Rocky Mountains and the Sierra Nevadas.

In summer they are usually found in the trees where they travel with the ease of acrobats; but in winter they stick more closely to the ground. Like the other musk-carriers, the marten has a pair of anal glands which give off a strong musk odor, but the smell is not as offensive as that of the weasel and mink.

A marten hunts day and night; besides red squirrels, it feeds on gray squirrels, chipmunks, rabbits, mice, birds, and bird eggs. It is known to eat some plant food, especially blueberries and the fruits of mountain ash. It prefers to catch wild prey, rarely raiding poultry houses or otherwise making a nuisance of itself. Its enemies are the larger carnivors, especially the fisher and the lynx.

A litter of three or four is born in spring, usually in a decaying trunk or hollow tree; the baby martens weigh about an ounce at birth. The young stay with their mother until three months of age. As they mature and develop their muscles, they playfully wrestle and chase each other up and down the tree trunks. When protected, as they are in the national parks, curiosity overcomes natural caution and they come close to camps where food is easily found. Martens are rugged animals, neither hibernating nor migrating in winter. The hair on the soles of their feet covers the pads and toes so that marten tracks in soft snow are almost circular in outline. Unlike the mink, the marten dislikes water and rarely catches its food in streams or swamps; it will cross a stream on a log rather than swim. One of its luxuries is to stretch out on a branch and take a sun bath.

FISHER. The unique distinction of the fisher lies in the fact that it is the fastest tree-traveler of all mammals. In spite of its name, the fisher, though liking to eat fish, does not catch it. The mistake may have come about because trappers could be sure of capturing a fisher if they baited the traps with fish. We have just learned that the marten is fast enough to catch the agile red squirrel; but the fisher in turn can catch the marten. In fact a fisher, although at a disadvantage in deep snow, can outrun even a snowshoe hare.

The fisher is the size of a fox, reaching a length of forty inches and a weight of eighteen pounds; it also has the bushy tail of a fox. But it can be recognized by the face characteristic of all members of the weasel family. The head is broad at the rear and tapers to a pointed muzzle. A fisher wears a dark-brown to grayish brown fur coat of soft silky hair; most of the animals trapped for the fur are caught in Canada. The fisher has never been very numerous in the United States; today its range is restricted to the cool conifer forests of northern New England and New York, and to the western mountains.

A fisher is active at all seasons, but usually hunts at night. Its prey are squirrels, chipmunks, marmots, rats, mice, rabbits, and the smaller carnivors including the marten. It is one of the few carnivors which has learned to cope with a porcupine. The fisher knocks this spiny-armored animal over with a stroke of its paw, then kills it by attack on its vulnerable underside. The quills seldom seem to bother the fisher. Occasionally a fisher may kill a deer trapped in the deep snow; it also will eat some plant food, such as fruits and nuts, when other food is not available.

A fisher's den is in a hollow tree or log, which may be lined with vegetation for some degree of comfort. A litter usually of three young are born here in April. The babies are helpless until their eyes open after seven weeks. By three months they have learned to take up the strenuous life of a hunter, and shift for themselves.

WOLVERINE. The chances today of encountering a wolverine are very slight indeed. This member of the weasel tribe never was common in the United States; it has long been extinct east of the Rocky Mountains. It is many years since Michigan, the Wolverine State, saw its last native wolverine. California estimates its wolverine population at only twenty-five or thirty in the entire state.

The wolverine, largest of the weasels, is a strange animal which looks like a bear and smells like a skunk; it

Wolverines, the largest of the weasel tribe, are rare carnivors which look like small bears and smell like skunks.

is little wonder that it also goes by the name of skunk-bear. The wolverine is a powerfully built animal with short bow legs and large feet armed with long claws. The long coarse fur is dark brown or black, with a broad whitish stripe extending along each side from shoulder to rump. Fullgrown individuals may be four feet in length and weigh thirty pounds. The fur is too bulky and the animals too scarce and hard to catch to be of any importance to trappers. Eskimos prize the fur for trimming their garments because the long guard hairs do not accumulate frost; this makes the fur excellent for edging the face opening of parka hoods.

Wolverines are cold-climate animals with bad-tempered dispositions and a preference for solitude. Strong and self-reliant, they can carry away prey much larger than themselves; they fear no other animal, and have been known to chase bear and mountain lion away from their kill and then to feast on the meal they have been forced to abandon. A wolverine misses no opportunity to pounce upon any large mammal which may be injured or bogged down in deep snow. Only the lowly porcupine occasionally gets revenge on this powerful hunter which is too clumsy to handle the spiny one with due respect. Wolverines are notorious gluttons because of their habit of eating whenever they can, and of consuming such huge quantities of meat at a sitting.

BADGER. The bow-legged, pigeon-toed, squat-bodied badger would hardly win a prize at a beauty contest, but on the other hand it is a remarkably energetic and independent member of the animal community. The flattened body is clothed with heavy fur of silvery gray, grizzled with brown and black. The dark-brown or black

The badger is a low-slung flat-bodied mammal with powerful digging claws and a "badge" of unique facial markings.

face is unmistakably marked with a white crescent around each eye. The common name is thought to have come from "badge" in reference to these unique facial markings. Large individuals reach a length of thirty inches and weigh up to twenty pounds. The fur is serviceable but not too valuable, and is used for collars and cuffs on fur coats. At one time the long guard hairs were much sought after in the manufacture of shaving brushes.

The badger is a powerful fighter, so fierce when cornered that it is usually left severely alone, even by hunting dogs. Its strong claws, which are always kept well-sharpened, are used chiefly for digging. A badger can dig into the ground so rapidly, using when necessary its mouth as well as all four feet, that the effect is a magician's disappearing act. While being pursued, the badger can fight off its attacker and at the same time dig its way into the ground and out of sight. Badgers get their meals by being able to dig faster than the moles, marmots, and pocket gophers they are pursuing. They also feed on mice, prairie dogs, and bird eggs. They often return to the same area and dig over the ground again, to be sure they have missed no tasty morsel. The resulting holes are a hazard to cattlemen since horses often break their legs by stepping in them.

A litter usually of three baby badgers is born in May or June, in an underground room. By autumn the youngsters are grown up, and with their parents fatten up on all the food they can find. During cold spells they take to their snug bedrooms and sleep for several weeks at a time. At intervals, especially during warm spells, they awaken to satisfy their hunger; then they return for another long nap. Badgers are generally found in dry open country throughout the central states and the West.

OTTER. This sleek animal looks as if it ought to be a first cousin of the seals rather than of the weasels. It is one of the most playful of all our native mammals. Young and old take time out from the serious business of eating and sleeping to wrestle, play tag, follow the leader, or toss stones; their favorite pastime is sliding down a slippery mud bank or snowy slope. When "coasting" they hold all four of their small feet close to the body and pointed backward. Otters are intelligent, affectionate animals with gentle dispositions; as a result they make interesting pets. Otters in captivity have lived to be nineteen years old.

Otters grow to four feet in length and weigh up to twenty or thirty pounds; the females are much smaller than the males. The dark-brown fur, almost black when wet, is our most durable pelt. The otter has no trouble in keeping warm in winter, even though it may spend much time in icy water; for beneath the thick underfur is the added protection of a layer of fat similar to the blubber of whales. The outer coat has long glistening guard hairs. The darkest pelts are considered the most valuable; these come from eastern Canada and northeastern United States. Most otter is trapped in Louisiana, New York, Maine, Washington, and Oregon. Otter is found in fresh-water streams and ponds, and in marine

Otters are well suited for life in the water as well as on land.

coves and estuaries, in every state. In spite of its wide distribution it is not abundant in any one locality.

Otters are well suited for life in the water. Provided by nature with webbed feet and a long muscular tail, they are expert swimmers and divers. Underwater they are as graceful in their movements as a seal. They feed on a variety of aquatic animals: crayfish, snails, clams, frogs, and other amphibians. They have a special fondness for salmon and trout, and hence compete with human fishermen. For this reason they are not particularly liked by man. Otters have a keen sense of smell and also of touch aided by sensitive whiskers. They travel in the water whenever possible for their absurdly short legs make land travel difficult.

SKUNK. A byword for unpleasant odor, the skunk utilizes to the maximum the advantage of the musk glands typical of the weasel family. Three common kinds of skunks live in the United States. The familiar striped skunk, found in every state, is identified by its black fur coat with two white stripes along the back which join over the shoulders and head. The spotted skunk of the southeastern and western states has a black coat whose white stripes are broken into irregular large spots. The hog-nosed skunk of the Southwest has a broad white cape over its entire back, terminating in a white tail. In all species the anal scent glands produce an oily, yellowish liquid which the skunk can eject as a spray, with surprisingly accurate aim. It has a reserve of this ammunition sufficient for five or six volleys, but usually has need of only one.

Skunks are by nature peaceable and friendly. When disturbed they give ample warning by stamping their feet, stiffening their front legs, clicking their teeth or growling. If these expressions of displeasure do not bring results, the dangerous warning signal of the erect tail is followed by having the skunk whip its body into a U-shape with both head and hind quarters facing the intruder. From this point on, the luckless victim is exposed to the most unpleasant form of chemical warfare known in the animal kingdom. As the hip muscles of the skunk contract, the liquid is sprayed to a distance of six to eight feet. For the unfortunate person who is within range of this spray, washing in water does little good. Gasoline, ammonia, or a dilute solution of sodium hypochlorite is the only effective deodorizer.

The familiar striped skunk is found in every state; when deprived of its musk glands it makes a safe and interesting pet.

Skunks usually hunt at night, and as a result many are killed by automobiles on our highways. In spring skunks feed on meadow mice, grasshoppers, beetles, crickets, and numerous insect larvae. In summer they shift to a vegetarian diet and eat fruits and berries and often raid vegetable gardens, as they have a strong liking for corn. Bees, poultry, and birds are also on the skunk menu. Since skunks are poor climbers, fencing in poultry is a protection against their attacks. Even with their occasional destroying of farm animals, a live skunk is worth much more than a dead one because insect and rodent pests are a main item of their diet.

In the northern states skunks retire to their dens in winter. They may dig their own burrows, or occupy a deserted woodchuck or fox den. Some skunks may winter above ground under a building or in a pile of stones. Often a number of skunks, especially females and young, may den together. The males are more active in winter than the females and hence are more frequently caught in traps. Thus the females escape capture, and the skunk population keeps increasing. Skunks are trapped for their fur which is used to make coats and jackets and for trimming. The winter sleep lasts a few months in the north, but by February the animals are active as the mating season begins. A litter of three to six young is born two months later; the young are born blind, toothless, and almost hairless. The eyes open at three weeks, and the young begin taking care of themselves when three months old.

Skunks are lucky animals in one respect; they are one of the few species which is better off with the advance of civilization than it was formerly. The destruction of forests has opened up large areas of brush and second growth which make ideal homes and feeding grounds for these animals. Skunks have recently become popular as pets, after being properly "deskunked," because of their amiable and friendly disposition.

The spotted skunk is smaller than the striped skunk, being about half the size of a housecat. It is an attractive little animal, nimble footed and dainty. This skunk has the unusual habit of standing on its forepaws when excited, but sinks back on all fours when its spraying mechanism goes into action.

The hog-nosed skunk has a long naked muzzle which it uses as a flexible snout in rooting for food. The fur is coarse and harsh, of little market value. This uncommon skunk has extra-long claws on the forefeet, used in scratching for insects and grubs in earth and decaying logs.

THE RACCOON FAMILY

RACCOON.   Nature may have thought she gave the coon a mark of distinction in the uniquely black-banded tail and grizzled gray fur. However their appeal to early Americans led to the coon-skin cap which was the mark of the true pioneering woodsman as well as to the raccoon coat which was at one time indispensable to the well-dressed collegian. Known as the "bear's small cousin," the coon is a medium-sized carnivor as large as a big housecat, weighing up to twenty-five pounds. It is easily recognized by the black mask across the small pointed face. Each foot has five toes, and the footprint is very much like that of a child. Raccoons are crafty animals and thus have managed to survive in every one of our states.

Their eating habits are not as specialized as those of other carnivors; in fact raccoons are omnivorous animals. Their favorite food is crayfish, which they hunt along the margins of streams, their long black fingers prying up the rocks and soil in search of hidden delicacies. Also on the coon menu are mussels, snails, frogs, and fish. When it finds its food in or near water, a raccoon often holds it underwater, washing off the dirt to clean it before eating. This has given rise to the popular idea that a coon always washes its food before it will eat. However where water is not available, the coon still eats what food it can find. Raccoons hide during the day, coming out at dusk to prowl for food. They tear rotted logs apart with their sharp claws in search for hidden grubs and insects; when bird eggs are discovered they are eaten with evident pleasure. In summer and fall they feast on berries and fruits; their fondness for corn and melons often gets them into trouble with the farmer. But coons are beneficial to the farmer too, for they eat many insects and grubs.

The den of a coon is in a hollow tree or a small opening in a rocky bank located near water where favorite food abounds. There are usually four in each litter of young, born in April or May. In the northern states, when food becomes scarce in winter, the raccoons retire to their dens and spend several months in a long sleep. During warm spells they awake, and catch up on their eating. Often several families of raccoons may den together. Coons are crafty woodsmen, hiding their trail by walking in the water at the edge of a stream to throw their pursuers off the scent. They are also excellent climbers and are often found in trees.

Coon meat is considered by some to be very tasty, so

that coons are hunted as food as well as for the fur. In colonial days, the pelts were used as money. The raccoon is a plucky fighter and is usually more than a match for even several hunting dogs. In spite of man, coons have managed to keep their numbers constant. They thrive in captivity, and make intelligent, if mischievous, pets. Raccoons have lived to be fourteen years old in captivity.

THE BEAR FAMILY

The largest carnivors on earth belong to the bear family. The huge bulk of a bear is clothed in a thick fur coat which enables the animal to endure winter weather in cold climates. The limbs are short and stout, with large flat feet which leave footprints somewhat like those of a man. Like the raccoon, bears are omnivors, without the highly specialized meat-eating teeth found in other carnivor families. Bears resemble dogs in having forty-two teeth, with a full set of incisors, canines, and premolars.

BLACK BEAR. A black bear may be any color from black or dark brown to the lighter shades of reddish brown and cinnamon. The lighter individuals are found in the West. Even though only five or six feet in length, and three feet high at the shoulders, bears are solid flesh and bone with weights up to six hundred pounds. Compared to the less common grizzly bear, the black bear has a straight profile and no hump over the shoulders. If black, the animal is undoubtedly a black bear; if it is some shade of brown, has humped shoulders and great size, one can identify it as a grizzly bear.

Black bears formerly ranged all over forested United States. Now they are scattered in the more secluded portions of New England and New York, the Appalachians,

Black bears are a star attraction at many of our national parks; they may also be dark brown to cinnamon color.

the Great Lakes states, Florida, and in the West. They are the star attraction in our western national parks, where they have prospered almost too well on the fare offered by tourists. In spite of warnings by the park rangers, many visitors underestimate the strength and unpredictable nature of the bears and are careless enough to be injured by teasing them.

The black bear is not a fussy eater. It believes in variety and loves such tidbits as honey, bees, and ants. It may prefer a meat meal but is too slow and clumsy to catch larger animals than chipmunks, ground squirrels, and marmots. Other meat items on the bear's menu are eggs, crickets, grasshoppers, and other prey ridiculously small for such a large animal. During the fawning season the black bear is on the lookout for baby deer, but has difficulty in locating the well camouflaged animals. A black bear is often forced by circumstances to be a vegetarian, feeding on grass, fruits, berries, bark of trees, bulbs, and roots. It moves along at a care-free, lumbering pace in its search for food, for it has few enemies. As winter approaches, a black bear will gorge itself on acorns and beechnuts, storing up a winter's supply of food in the form of a thick layer of body fat.

Having eaten all it can possibly hold, the black bear becomes semi-dormant, curling up for a long sleep which, in the northern states, may last from October until April. Its bed may be in a den or hollow log, but more often it lies on the ground in the shelter of a fallen tree or pile of brush. Winter snows may pile high on its shaggy fur, but bruin sleeps on just the same. The mother bear, while still asleep, gives birth to her cubs, of which there usually are twins; this event happens in January. Bear cubs are unusually tiny at birth, being only nine inches in length and weighing less than a pound; the helpless cubs are blind, hairless, and toothless. Snuggled in the warm fur of the mother, they nurse continuously and grow in size, acquiring a black downy coat. By February they have opened their eyes, and when the warm days of early spring arrive the mother bestirs herself and takes her cubs out into the world. The cubs now weigh about four pounds. They romp and play like kittens, and have an uncanny ability to get into mischief. But their mother is a stern disciplinarian, teaching them the more serious business of life: how to hunt mice and dig for roots, how to watch out for danger, and how to swim. The happy bear family roams the woods until autumn when again they prepare for a long winter sleep. In nature black bears may live to be fifteen years old; in captivity they have lived for twenty-four years.

GRIZZLY BEAR. These huge carnivors, eight or nine feet in length and weighing up to sixteen hundred pounds, were the subject of many fantastic tales by early explorers. Today, like many other of our large mammals, grizzlies are very rare in the United States. It is estimated that there are only five or six hundred individuals left, and these are in Yellowstone, Teton, and Glacier National Parks. With its size and strength, a grizzly bear fears no animal and certainly could make short work of an unarmed man.

The fur of a grizzly bear is brownish or yellowish, often with a grizzled tip to the hairs, a feature which is responsible for the name. Like the black bear, it is omnivorous and feeds on the same variety of animal and plant food. It is a better fisherman than the black bear; in the far north grizzlies have become proficient at catching salmon. A grizzly bear has the strength to kill and carry away a bull elk. In spite of its bulk, it can travel surprisingly fast; it has been clocked at thirty miles per hour. Grizzlies make a beeline when they travel, leaving trails which go straight across ridges and through obstacles which would divert a black bear. Some of these trails have been worn deep by a succession of bears treading in each others footsteps.

The eyesight of a grizzly bear is poor, but this is offset by excellent hearing and sense of smell. In fact the nose seems to be the most sensitive part of the body in search-

A grizzly bear can be recognized by its huge size and dished-in profile.

ing for food. If a grizzly bear smells a hidden rodent, it may turn over huge areas of soil in a search for the possible meal. Unlike black bears, grizzlies rarely climb trees. The twin cubs are born in winter while the mother is asleep in her den; they require eight years to grow to full size. As soon as they take care of themselves they become solitary individuals; grizzlies dislike each others' company as well as that of other animals. Like the black bear, a grizzly can live to be quite old; in captivity the life span is thirty years.

THE DOG FAMILY

The wild members of the dog family have many physical traits and habits in common with the domesticated dog. Most of the species are sociable, living in family units or larger packs. The parents are attentive to their pups, and teach them how to hunt for their meals and avoid their enemies. Many of the species are very intelligent and have been able to survive in spite of persecution. Others have been driven out of their original homes and are now rare in states where they were once common.

RED FOX. This fox could easily be mistaken for a small dog as it trots across a farmer's field. Unlike many other wild animals, the red fox seems to enjoy the challenge of living dangerously by staying close to man even though the farmer, trapper, and hunter unite in an attempt to take its life. The symbol of cunning, the red fox relies on its wits to keep out of trouble.

The favorite home of the red fox is a mixture of farmland and woods; it is rarely found in the deep forest. It is clever in hiding its tracks and avoiding capture, although it is not a fast runner nor does it have much endurance. Mice, shrews, weasels, rabbits, muskrats, pheasants, turtles and turtle eggs, eggs of birds and even the birds themselves comprise its diet. When larger prey is not at hand, a red fox is satisfied with crickets, grasshoppers, and beetles. In winter it often digs through the snow to get at frozen apples.

The red fox trots along gracefully and quietly on its padded feet; a sharp face, bright eyes, and erect ears give the impression of an alert mind. It stalks its prey cautiously until near enough to pounce upon it suddenly. Like many members of the dog family, it caches what meat it cannot eat at the first sitting. Its particular bad habit is raiding poultry yards, but in spite of this the red fox is more friend than foe to the farmer.

A pair of foxes usually remains together for a year, sometimes longer. The father and mother fox both take care of the family. The parents select a den, which often has been used the year before by different foxes. The den may be a hidden cozy room off an underground tunnel; in it four to nine pups are born in March or April. The father brings food to the nursing mother, and later to the young foxes. When five weeks old they venture outdoors and are as playful as domesticated puppies. As they grow older they learn to hunt for their own meals, and to avoid their enemies the coyotes, wolves, bobcats, and lynxes. The numbers of red foxes have remained fairly constant, in spite of their natural enemies and man; the reduction in the number of larger carnivors has given the red fox a better chance of survival.

GRAY FOX. Slightly smaller than the red fox, the gray fox is a grizzled gray and black animal with black face and muzzle, and a long slender tail. This species is a warm-climate animal, found in the southeastern and western states, although in recent years it has been extending its range northward. It is the only fox which is likely to be found climbing a tree, but it does this usually only to escape pursuers. It is less crafty than the red fox, but knows enough to shun man by remaining in the safety of the swamps and woods. The gray fox depends upon rodents and rabbits for most of its food, although at times it will eat grass, nuts, and fruits. The fur is too coarse to be of much value to trappers.

KIT FOX. So named because of its small size, this shy member of the dog family avoids contact with humans as much as the red fox seems to welcome it. Only two or three feet in length, it stands a foot high at the shoulders and weighs about four pounds. This fox has a gray or buff fur coat, with lighter underparts, and a black-tipped tail. Being unsuspicious and trusting, the kit fox is hunted and easily trapped. Thus it is not very abundant today in any part of its range, which extends from Kansas and Colorado westward and southward. It travels and hunts mostly at night, spending the days underground or in a hidden resting place. This fox can run faster than any of its relatives; for the hundred-yard dash it is perhaps the speediest mammal. While running it zig-zags quicker than the eye can follow, and uses this dodging technique to escape its pursuers. A kit fox eats kangaroo rats, pocket mice, ground squirrels, rabbits, beetles and grasshoppers.

COYOTE. The picture of a buffalo may call to mind the wide open spaces, but the call of the coyote is the sound most associated with the plains. This wild dog is a remarkable vocalist, with a singing range that covers two full octaves. His nocturnal serenading is such a variety of barks, whines, howls, and wails that it seems more like a chorus of four or five coyotes than only one.

The coyote was first seen by the Spaniards; they called

it by its Aztec name which was coyotl; this became the Mexican ki-o-tee which is the correct way to pronounce our Americanized version. In some states it is also known as the brush wolf or prairie wolf. Coyotes are typically dwellers of the open plains and shrubby deserts, although in recent years they have adapted themselves to a wide range of habitats. Fifty years ago they were unknown east of Wisconsin and Texas. Today they have wandered as far east as Maine and Florida. Their rapid increase can be accounted for by their unusual adaptability and cunning, which is often more than a match for man himself.

A coyote resembles a sharp-faced collie with a brownish gray coat; it is much larger and heavier than a fox. The coarse thick fur may be a grizzled gray, a yellowish or tawny color, or on the black shade. The underparts are whitish and the tail is tipped with black. Large individuals may reach a length of five feet and weigh up to twenty-five pounds. Coyotes travel at a dog trot or lope, but can run as fast as thirty miles an hour on open ground. They eat anything that is edible, and often much that is not; they are the garbage collectors of the prairies. Their usual diet consists of mice and squirrels; in winter they hunt for crayfish, frogs, and what is left of autumn's fruits and berries. Coyotes will eat carrion as well as fresh meat. By hunting in packs, they have learned to attack large prey such as deer. At times they develop an unfortunate taste for sheep and other domestic animals and thus become a menace to cattlemen, who hunt them mercilessly.

Coyotes mate for a year, or longer. The prospective parents select a den which may be a hollow log or small

– 118 –

cave, or may be a deep burrow with an underground bedroom. The litter of coyote pups may be as large as sixteen, but the number is usually five or six. They are born in March or April. The father coyote is quite devoted to his family, and carries food home to his mate and to the pups when they are old enough to share it. As the pups grow they resemble playful domesticated puppies, except for their bigger ears and smaller eyes. Both parents teach the youngsters how to hunt for mice and rabbits, and other necessary facts of coyote life. When able to shift for themselves the young coyotes have to find

Coyotes are wild "dogs" with an unusual adaptability which has resulted in their spread eastward to the Atlantic Coast.

new territory, which often means a journey of a hundred miles from their birthplace. Coyote pups can be brought up like dogs; coyotes will breed with dogs, but the resulting cross produces nervous and untamable animals.

WOLF. The wolf, in fiction, is the villain of the animal world, the savage killer which is as likely to attack man as another animal. There is no doubt that a healthy fullgrown wolf has the strength and the stamina to tackle any living American mammal. Six or seven feet in length, standing three feet tall at the shoulders, and powered with a hundred pounds of muscle, the wolf can certainly take on all comers. Wolves have been practically eliminated from the populous areas of the country and today are found only in small numbers in the inaccessible portions of the Great Lakes area and in the West. Because of its appetite and size, a wolf needs a large home territory of perhaps several hundred square miles. Its chief food consists of mice, ground squirrels, and gophers. By hunting in packs, wolves can follow elk, deer, and antelope herds and single out stragglers and weaklings for the kill. Wolves are not fast runners; twenty miles per hour is considered their top speed.

Like the coyote, the wolf father is a good parent, assisting in feeding and bringing up his pups. Mating begins in January or February, when a den site is selected. The den is often an enlarged fox or badger burrow. Later the litter of four to ten pups are born. The father wolf has been known to carry back heavy prey as far as ten miles to his hungry mate and youngsters. The family unit, consisting of the father, mother, pups, and some uncles and aunts, is an important social group. Family units unite to form the larger wolf packs. Wolves are never

The timber wolf is unmistakably a member of the dog family.

abundant in spite of their brute strength, intelligence, and social habits; they are kept in check by lack of food and by disease, especially rabies. Under ideal conditions a wolf might live to be sixteen years of age. Old experienced wolves can become a serious menace to livestock, continuing to raid cattle herds in spite of traps and hunters. But as a rule, a wolf likes to keep out of man's way and is usually successful in avoiding him.

THE CAT FAMILY

The wild members of the cat family are the most powerful hunters among the carnivors. Yet, except for their size and coloring, they are remarkably like the common housecat. They have teeth which are highly specialized for meat-eating, particularly the dagger-like canines and the high-crowned cheek teeth with their sharp shearing edges. Cougar, jaguar, and ocelot have thirty teeth; the lynx and the bobcat have twenty-eight. There are five toes on the forepaws, four on the hindpaws; in the footprints however the fifth toe is rarely seen. The long sharp claws can be pulled back into their sheaths so that they are not worn out needlessly. These retractile claws do not show in the footprints, as do the claws of dogs. Soft fleshy pads on the soles of the feet enable these carnivors to move noiselessly in stalking their prey. Although spending most of their lives on the ground, cats take to the trees when pursued; they dislike water and will rarely swim of their own choice. The eyes are adapted for night vision; as a result, the pupils are very large at night, but mere slits in the daytime.

BOBCAT.   Also known as the wildcat, this species is the most widely distributed of all our native cats. It is found in practically every state, but being nocturnal and extremely wary, it is rarely seen. The bobcat is not a large carnivor, being little larger than a housecat and rarely weighing more than fifteen pounds. Yet it is a scrappy fighter and when cornered becomes a demon of fury. This undoubtedly is the origin of the expression "he can lick his weight in wildcats."

A bobcat's fur is reddish brown, streaked with black; the underparts are a spotted white. The most unusual feature of this cat is the short stump of a tail, which is responsible for its name. The only other bob-tailed cat is the larger lynx which has longer and clumsier limbs. Both animals have tufts of hair on their ears, but those of the bobcat are much shorter. The fur of a bobcat is not highly prized, being used chiefly for inexpensive coat trimming. Bobcats have a surly and vicious disposition, rarely making friends with man in captivity.

The den of a bobcat is likely to be under a rocky ledge or in a thicket; from this it emerges after sunset in its search for rabbits and rodents, which it stalks by a keen sense of smell as well as of sight. During the mating season the bobcat, like the domesticated cat, becomes vigorously vocal. The male gives way to a noisy succession of screams, yowls, and wails commonly referred to as "caterwauling." These serenades to the female cats are heard mostly in January and February. About six weeks later two or three kittens are born in the den; their fur is spotted and their eyes are closed. By June the growing kittens are out hunting their own food. The youngsters often remain together, with their parents, for the first year.

Bobcats are likely to be found in any kind of habitat as long as there is some wooded cover in which to hide. They do not range as far into the colder northern states and Canada as the lynx since they are not as well adapted for winter living. When chasing prey in deep snow, the bobcat sinks in and has a struggle to overtake its victim.

Because of the habit of raiding farmyards, the bobcat has been almost exterminated in the populated eastern states where bounties have been in effect for many years. Such bounties for dead bobcats were common in New England during the last century.

LYNX.   This Arctic member of the cat family is very much at home in the rigorous climate of Canada and Alaska. It ranges southward into the northern portion of the United States wherever there are deep forests, as in northern New England and New York, and in Washington and Oregon. Lynx was once found as far south as Pennsylvania and Indiana. It is a confirmed forest dweller, rarely seen in the scrub woods where bobcat may be found. Logging and forest fires have destroyed much of its original home.

A lynx resembles a large housecat with absurdly long legs and big, clumsy feet. Other features are the bob-tail and the tufted ears, and a dignified ruff of hair on its cheeks. A full-grown lynx stands two feet high at the shoulders, and weighs up to forty pounds. The winter coat, of thick warm fur, is gray tinged with brown; the summer coat is lighter in weight and more definitely brownish. The big feet serve the lynx well, for they act as snowshoes and keep the lynx from floundering in deep snow when pursuing its favorite prey, the snowshoe rabbit, or catching an occasional deer. The sides and soles of the lynx's feet are covered with long hairs which also are an aid in staying on the surface of the snow. The lynx feeds on squirrels, mice, and partridge. It is an active hunter the year round, with few enemies other than man, who traps it for the thick soft fur which comes in a number of pastel shades.

A lynx resembles a large house cat with absurdly long legs, clumsy feet and a bobtail.

The den of a lynx may be in a rocky crevice or a hollow tree. Here a litter of from one to four kittens are born in spring. The young are precocious, with eyes nearly open at birth and an ability to stand within a few hours. Their reddish or buff coats are striped or blotched. At four months they are able to go on hunting trips with their mother. A lynx in captivity lived to be twelve years old.

COUGAR. No other mammal is known by so many different local names; panther, mountain lion, catamount, puma, and painter are a few. Also not many other mammals have so many unfounded tales based on their ferocity and incredible exploits. Formerly this American lion ranged throughout the forested portions of our country;

today it is common only in Florida, along the Gulf coast, and westward in the Rocky Mountains and Sierra Nevadas. There have been occasional recent records of cougar in Maine and the Great Lakes states. Even in its natural range a cougar is a rare animal.

With a muscular and well coordinated body, the cougar is the trim athlete of the mammals; weighing in at two hundred pounds, it has few opponents to fear. Like the grizzly bear, it could dispose of an unarmed man very quickly if it wanted to. Fortunately it usually minds its own business, perhaps on the assumption that human flesh is less desirable eating than deer or sheep. Male cougars, which are larger than the females, reach a length of seven feet. The soft close fur is a tawny or reddish brown in summer, grayish in winter; the underparts are paler and the tail has a dark tip.

The cougar has the reputation of being a dangerous killer, but actually there are only a few authentic records of attacks on human beings. Because of the deeds of a few individuals, the entire cougar clan has been outlawed. There are instances where they have learned to live the easy way by preying on defenseless sheep, cattle, and horses. But their natural food consists of the large hoofed mammals, and so they are a check on excessive populations of deer.

The den of the cougar is a roomy crevice or cave in a rocky cliff; since the cougar does not retire for the winter, it is used chiefly at family-raising time. Here the mother gives birth to kittens, usually twins, each about a foot in length and weighing a pound. Their pale tan coats are very different from their parents', being spotted with dark brown and ringed with brown on the tail. After their eyes

– 126 –

The conspicuously-marked ocelot has its home in Texas along the Rio Grande River.

open, they play like domestic kittens. A few have been kept as pets; but they grow rapidly, at six months weighing forty pounds. Although they learn to keep their claws sheathed, their size and power make them a dangerous pet. Adult cougars are said to scream in a shrill, high-pitched tone calculated to chill the blood of the bravest hunter. Ordinarily, however, they are silent hunters, roaming the woods noiselessly in the search of some tempting mammal. They may range twenty or thirty miles from their den in their quest. After a kill, they cover what is left from their meal with a pile of brush, and return later to finish the repast.

OCELOT. Two members of the cat family are rather rare visitors to the United States from the land south of the Rio Grande. These are the ocelot and jaguar, which occur in great numbers in Central and South America. The ocelot is the smaller of the two, reaching a length of four feet and thus being about twice the size of a housecat. Its home is among the thickets fringing the Rio Grande River, in southern Texas; here it is also known as the tiger cat and leopard cat.

The ocelot is a handsome animal, with a short-haired yellow coat decorated with a variety of black spots, rings, bars, and blotches in a riotous pattern, as if dressed for a carnival. Ocelots are easily tamed and make fine pets; their inoffensive nature persists even when cornered, for they rarely put up much of a fight. A captured ocelot seems more philosophical than the spitting, snarling lynx or bobcat. The food of an ocelot is a variety of small animals; snakes, rats, birds, rabbits. It hunts mostly at night, and climbs and swims with ease.

JAGUAR. This American leopard resembles the true leopard of Africa and Asia so closely that often the skins of the two cannot be told apart. The yellowish brown fur is marked with black rosettes, some of which have spots in the center. The head is large, the legs short and muscular, and the tail long and heavy. Slightly shorter in total length than a cougar, a jaguar has the advantage of weight; large specimens weigh two hundred to two hundred fifty pounds.

Jaguars occasionally come into the United States, in southern Arizona and New Mexico. They once roamed southern California also, but have been extinct there since 1860. Jaguars climb well, and often lie in the trees waiting for their prey to appear. When they pounce on it from above, the force of the impact usually breaks the neck of the victim. Jaguars hunt along waterways in the forests, feeding on deer, peccary, crocodiles, alligators, and fish. They have no fear of the water, and swim easily. Like other large carnivors, jaguars at times take a liking to livestock. But for the most part they are not aggressive killers in areas where man lives and has his farms.

*

These are some of the native relatives of our familiar pets, the dogs and cats. Knowing the habits of the wild species helps to better understand some of the innate traits in our pets which are difficult to change; a cat capturing a canary or attempting to get a goldfish out of the bowl is only following an inherited urge. The large carnivors are a fascinating segment of our native wild life, and should be protected against extinction just as much as the less aggressive hoofed animals. Undoubtedly you will never encounter most of these carnivors in your nature explorations; but at least you can see them in the national parks and wild-life refuges, where they are being preserved for posterity in as natural living conditions as possible.

The California sea lion is a playful, intelligent mammal which has become well-adapted for life in the sea.

CHAPTER FIVE

THE SEA-GOING MAMMALS

Being land-dwellers ourselves, we can appreciate the problems mammals face in living on land. We have already seen how the body structure and activities of three large groups of mammals—the rodents, the hoofed animals, and the carnivors—are suited to various land habitats. Biologists have acquired considerable information about the lives of the mammals that live on land, and even we, as naturalists, are likely to come across some mammals on our explorations. The vast realm of the sea and the animals which live in it are, on the other hand, an almost unknown world. Our knowledge of marine life is based chiefly on that found near the shore or in the upper reaches of the open sea. The sea has a great fascination for land-dwellers and, among the mammals, quite a few species have abandoned the land to live in the sea. The story of mammal life would be very incomplete if it did not note the versatility of the mammal body in adapting itself to aquatic life.

The land and water environments are not separated by a biological barrier which prevents migration in either direction. In the very distant geologic past all animals were aquatic. The first vertebrates of which there is any fossil record lived in the water: they were the fishes. Fish possess a structure and accompanying fitness for living underwater. Their streamlined bodies are covered with scales which reduce surface friction; they have muscular tails so they can swim swiftly in such a dense medium as water; and they are endowed with gills for breathing under water. Fish are the best adapted of all vertebrates for living in lakes, streams, and oceans.

In succeeding geological periods descendants of fish-type ancestors crossed the seashore barrier and accommodated themselves to life on land. As amphibians, they possessed limbs instead of fins, and lungs instead of gills. However, they never became completely free of the bonds which tied them to the water. Even today most of the amphibians return to the water to lay their eggs.

Millions of years after the first clumsy amphibians crawled over the land, newer types of land-dwellers appeared which gave rise to the present-day reptiles and mammals. These animals were more completely converted for land-dwelling, with bodies and biological activities far different from those of fish. With these special adaptations, mammals have been able to colonize the woods and meadows, the deserts and high mountains, often far removed from the sea.

Just as the borderline between sea and shore was no obstacle for the migration of animal life landward, neither has it been a barrier preventing some mammal species from going back to the water to live. In doing this, the species has retained much of the basic body pattern of a land-dweller, especially in the internal organs. Evolution is not reversible however; no mammal can become a fish. Yet mammal species have accomplished wonders in adapting themselves to living in the water. Some of them, as the porpoise, have come to resemble fish so closely that they are often mistaken for them.

A few mammal species have taken to the water to seek a home or get their food. This is true of the muskrat, beaver, mink, and otter which show varying degrees of adaptation to aquatic life. Of these the otter has undergone the greatest change from a typical mammal; its slender supple body moves like a seal through the water, and its short limbs with webbed feet are more useful in the water than on land.

Other mammals have severed ties with the land far more completely. If you live along our seacoast or have vacationed by the edge of the sea, you may have caught a glimpse of some of these marine mammals. The harbor seal is found along both our coasts, and its relative, the sea lion, is a familiar sight off the Pacific coast. Porpoises and dolphins often come into harbors and river estuaries where they can be seen from bridges and piers. Occasionally a whale is cast up on a beach, giving landlubbers an opportunity to see at close range one of the most unusual of all mammals.

A mammal, in order to become completely aquatic, must undergo changes in its body structure to fit it for living in the water rather than on land. Some of these changes are external and obvious, such as those involving body contour, body covering, and limbs. Others are internal and deal with eating, breathing, and the senses. Many of these changes make the mammal resemble a fish.

The shape of the body is not too important in a land animal. A bulky body, long legs, various projections in the form of ears and horns, and a shaggy coat are usually no hindrance at the speeds most mammals travel against the resistance of only air. But as engineers have learned in designing craft to travel on or under water, body styling is of utmost importance. A streamlined, spindleshaped body is essential, with as little resistance as possible at the bow and a minimum of drag at the stern. The head of an aquatic mammal is therefore smaller and more pointed than its land counterpart; its neck is shorter or has disappeared entirely; its body has become slender and tapers at both ends.

The surface of a body moving through the water must be as free as possible of any projections which might increase friction. Fur coats are a handicap to swimmers. For this reason, that biological badge of a mammal, the fur coat, is very short and compact or has been practically eliminated. In the porpoises and whales all that is left of the hairy coat is a bristly whisker or two around the snout. In the aquatic mammals, external ears are small or absent; the nostrils are situated on the top of the head.

Other changes involve the limbs. As "frog men" have discovered, the expanded surface of a foot-paddle provides greater force to drive a body through the water. Many aquatic mammals have webbed feet with very elongated toes. This makes possible an oar-type propulsion. More effective, however, is a side-to-side movement of body and tail, which is the way a fish swims. The streamlined porpoise can attain by this type of movement speeds of forty miles per hour. Other completely aquatic mammals, such as the whales, also swim in this fashion. When limbs are not used, they tend to become smaller or disappear; thus whales, porpoises, and manatees have no external hindlimbs at all. In the whale there is a special horizontal fluke on either side of the tail. By moving these flukes up and down, independently of each other, the whale creates a propeller-like thrust which moves its great bulk through the water with ease.

A number of interesting internal changes have taken place in mammal species which have become aquatic, most significant being the adaptation of lung-breathing to underwater life. Aquatic mammals must come to the surface to breathe, even though they have learned to hold their breath much longer than any land mammal. This rising to the surface for air varies from several times a minute for the porpoise, to intervals of thirty or forty-five minutes for the whale. When a whale surfaces, the warm air is forcibly breathed out through the nostrils, or blowholes, and spouts upward as a column ten to twenty feet in height. It often resembles a stream of water because of the condensation of the moisture in the breath. This has given rise to the misconception that whales take in water through the mouth and eject it through the blowhole. The air passage from the nostril goes directly to the lungs; thus water cannot possibly get into the lungs from the mouth.

Except for the manatee, all marine mammals are carnivorous. Their food consists of fish, small crustaceans, mollusks, and microscopic invertebrates. The sea is such an abundant source of these tiny animals that they can be scooped up by the mammals as they move through the water with open mouth. Teeth are not necessary for seizing and chewing this soup-like food; as a result, many marine mammals have poorly developed teeth or none at all. The toothless whales have a substitute in the form of an ingenious straining mechanism in the mouth, known as whalebone. Triangular plates of this material, with fringed edges, hang downward from the roof of the mouth. Small animals are strained from the seawater when the whale forces its tongue upward and thus expels water from the sides of its mouth. Mammals brought with them into the sea environment a priceless heritage of their land evolution: a highly developed brain. Fish have very simple brains, capable of only a low level of mental activity. Equipped with superior brain power, marine mammals have little difficulty in solving the problems of life in the sea.

SEALS AND SEA LIONS

Seals and sea lions belong to the order *Pinnipedia* (meaning fin feet), closely related to the order of the carnivors. Thus these aquatic animals are first cousins to the dogs, cats, and bears. They have a particularly close resemblance to the otter, and therefore are considered by some biologists to have originated from otter-like ancestors. Pinnipeds have had to compromise with the demands of living both on land and in the water. They reach their greatest development in cold climates and so are far more abundant in Canadian and Alaskan waters than along the seacoast of the United States. In all species the body is sleek and tapering, with short tail and small pointed head provided with teeth in both jaws. There are fewer incisors and more molars than in the land carnivors. Seals' teeth are not adequate for chewing so they bolt their food whole; their diet consists of fish, crustaceans, and mollusks. A seal's limbs are flippers with unusually long digits. A mass of fatty tissue (blubber) underlying the skin is a protection in icy water but makes a cumbersome body for land movement. Graceful and powerful swimmers in the water, on land seals and sea lions are handicapped by their paddle-like limbs.

Two families of pinnipeds live in the United States: the eared seals and the earless seals. The eared seals are also called fur seals and sea lions. In addition to small ears, fur seals can be recognized by their long forelimbs and relatively shorter hindlimbs; the latter are used to some extent in land locomotion because they are free of the tail, and can bend forward. The earless seals are also called hair seals or harbor seals. They have no external ears, the forelimbs are smaller than the hindlimbs, and the latter are fused with the tail so that they cannot rotate forward. Thus a harbor seal moves very awkwardly on land, by a caterpillar-like humping of the body. Various kinds of pinnipeds have long been hunted by man for their soft fur, their edible flesh, and as a source of oil for illumination and lubrication.

CALIFORNIA SEA LION. A visitor to San Francisco can see herds of sea lions on "seal rocks" and elsewhere along the California coast. Playful and intelligent, these supple animals are the trained seals of stage and circus. They are the universal entertainers at zoos throughout the country, where their honking bark and acrobatic stunts always attract a crowd. A sea lion has yellowish

– 137 –

to dark-brown, close fur which becomes shiny-black when wet. The average male grows to a length of seven or eight feet, and weighs 500 to 600 pounds. In addition to their greater size, the bulls differ from the cows in having a small mane and prominent crest along the top of the head. Sea-lion families are raised ashore. Each cow has a single brownish black pup, born in June or July. The pup learns to swim in the safety of the tidal pools, but by the end of the summer is at home in the rough water where it joins its parents and relatives. In captivity sea lions are long-lived animals, sometimes attaining twenty-five years in age. Their natural food consists of squid and fish. Because of their liking for fish, sea lions are a nuisance to fishermen, getting into the nets and eating the catch.

NORTHERN FUR SEAL. This is the valuable fur seal which breeds on the Pribiloff Islands in the Bering Sea. When migrating it sometimes appears off the west coast of the United States. The fur coat is dark gray to brown, with underparts and flippers of reddish brown. Fullgrown bulls are six or seven feet long and weigh 400 to 500 pounds. This seal has an unusual family life, each bull acquiring a harem of as many as forty cows. Each cow has a single glossy-black pup born in July on the rocky breeding grounds. Fur seals feed on fish, squid, and various shellfish. They spend most of their lives in the water. A seal pup requires several months to learn to swim, under the guidance of its mother. Seals are capable divers, one recorded dive being to a depth of 240 feet. The northern fur seal, as were other fur-bearers, was so exploited by hunters that by 1910 an original herd of some 1,500,000 individuals had been reduced to 132,000.

The capture of fur seals was then regulated by international agreement, so that by 1940 the herd had regained its original size. Fur seals obtained a reprieve from extinction also by the introduction of muskrat fur as "Hudson seal," which lessened the demand for true seal pelts.

HARBOR SEAL. This is the familiar and widely distributed seal of both our seacoasts. It is sometimes called the leopard seal because of the dark-brown spots on the yellowish gray coat. The hairy coat is very different from the soft fur of a sea lion. Harbor seals stick close to shore, being usually found near harbors and bays where they can be seen sunning themselves on rocks and ledges exposed by the falling tide. When thus basking they are wary and noisily plunge into the water at the slightest sign of danger. However, when safely in the water they are much more at ease, and bob vertically with ill-disguised curiosity to see what is going on. Their dog-like barking and small pointed dog-like faces reveal their relationship to the land carnivors.

Harbor seals are small animals, usually four or five feet in length with an average weight of 220 pounds. On adults the spots on the back tend to merge into an even dark color. As in all the earless seals, a tiny opening leads into a channel from the outside to the inner ear. This is open when the seal is on land, but automatically closes tightly when the animal is under water.

The pups are born on the rocks, in the spring or early summer. The first coat of the baby seal is of silky white fur, and is usually shed just before birth. Occasionally, however, a newborn pup retains the white coat for a few days. Ordinarily a baby seal is gray above and silvery white beneath. Seal pups are about thirty inches long at birth, and weigh about twenty-five pounds. They take to the water at once, but must come ashore to nurse. In six weeks they are weaned and feed on the usual fish and shellfish eaten by all marine animals of this family. A seal usually swims within sight of bottom while searching for a meal, and can make up to fifteen miles per hour. Harbor seals are rarely hunted since their fur is useless. Like the sea lion, harbor seals often annoy fishermen by becoming entangled in their nets and feeding on their catch.

WHALES, PORPOISES, AND DOLPHINS

Whales, porpoises, and dolphins belong to the order of mammals known as *Cetacea;* members of this group have changed considerably in appearance from a typical land mammal. The smooth, hairless body is sheathed in a thick layer of fat, or blubber. This acts as a heat insulator which is probably of value to those species living in Arctic and Antarctic seas. This insulating layer is so effective that when a whale is stranded on a beach and dies, the body loses heat slowly and decomposition takes place rapidly with the resulting formation of a great deal of gas. The layer of blubber also acts as a food reserve, and at the same time reduces the specific gravity of the huge body making it more buoyant. It is possible that the blubber provides an elastic covering which adjusts to the volume changes brought about when whales dive to great depths, as they often do. A cable-repair ship once hoisted a sperm whale from a depth of 3240 feet where it had become entangled with a submarine cable. At this depth the whale's body was subjected to a pressure of approximately 1400 pounds per square inch.

The external shape of cetaceans varies from the sleek streamlined body of a dolphin or porpoise to the apparently clumsy, blunt-headed body of a sperm whale. In all cases the fur coat has vanished, except for a few hairs around the snout; a harbor porpoise has only two to four hairs about its mouth, as proof that its ancestors once had fur covering. The tail of a cetacean is not flattened vertically like that of a fish, but is part of a horizontal propulsion mechanism with a flattened fluke on either side. By means of this a whale can move through the water as fast as a ship, and can rise or dive almost vertically.

A whale's forelimbs are flattened paddle-like fins, whose chief use is not for locomotion but as stabilizers. A dead whale, with this balancing control gone, floats on its side. The forelimb of a toothed whale has five digits, that of a whalebone whale, four. Externally there is no trace of hindlimbs in a cetacean. Buried in the flesh, however, are small remnants of hip bones as evidence that they once did have hindlimbs. The whale skeleton is made up of bones which are spongy and oil-soaked.

In some species the head has become unusually large, being a third or a quarter of the entire body length. The mouth is often a cavernous opening which could accommodate a couple of full-sized men. The nostrils, high on the head, are given the name of blowholes. The eyes are relatively small, and usually located low on the sides of the head, near the mouth. The lungs are huge and elastic, capable of holding a tremendous reserve of air. Yet whales can never live out of water, in spite of their mammal heritage of lungs; a stranded whale soon dies of suffocation, its weak chest crushed by the weight of the surrounding body. The young are born in the water, and are fed milk; the mother usually turns partly on her side and thus makes it possible for the baby to nurse out of water.

The cetaceans include seven families and at least forty species which frequent North American waters; many of them are rare today due to over-zealous whaling. They comprise two groups: the toothed whales and the toothless whales. The toothed whales have teeth in one or both jaws and are represented by the dolphins, porpoises, and sperm whale. The toothless whales have a substitute for teeth in the form of whalebone. There is a longitudinal row of whalebone plates on each side of the roof of the mouth; in each row the plates or sheets hang crosswise, each plate being triangular with the broad base at the top and frayed at the inner margin. The individual pieces of whalebone average a half inch in thickness. All the plates of whalebone act as a strainer, so that small forms of animal life taken into the whale's mouth with the water are caught as the water is forced out again. Common toothless whales are the finback, sulphur-bottom, humpbacked, Greenland, and right whales.

COMMON DOLPHIN. This seafarer usually stays far from land, and prefers warmer water than most whales. Dolphins travel in schools, and have the habit of playfully romping about ships, racing alongside or leaping across the bow. All true dolphins have a beaked profile; the beak of the common dolphin is six inches long, separated from the forehead by a groove. The fish-like body reaches a length of nine or ten feet, the upper part being black, the sides wavy bands of yellow, black, or white; the under surface is light gray. The back fin has a distinctive swept-back design. As in all the dolphins and porpoises, there is but a single blowhole.

The bottle-nosed dolphins in captivity at Marineland, Florida, have been trained to leap out of the water when offered food.

BOTTLE-NOSED DOLPHIN. A dolphin frequently seen along the Atlantic coast as far north as New Jersey, the bottle-nose thrives in captivity. It is a star attraction at Marineland, Florida, where the dolphins have been trained to leap out of the water and take food from their trainer's hand. A related species occurs on the Pacific coast. This is a large dolphin, growing to a length of twelve feet, with a three-inch beak. It has a dark-gray upper surface and lighter under surface. Schools of these dolphins often migrate into inshore waters.

Common use of the term "dolphin" has led to much confusion. A species of fish is known as dolphin, and a species of dolphin is known as blackfish. This dolphin, also called pilot whale, is a blunt-nosed mammal twenty-eight feet in length. Still another species of dolphin is the killer whale, a black and white animal thirty feet long with rounded head, high back fin and a battery of big sharp teeth. Killer whales are the ferocious predators of the sea, traveling in packs like wolves and attacking seals, sea lions, porpoises, and even whales. For a ravenous appetite one can hardly equal the record of a twenty-one-foot killer whale which had remains of thirteen porpoises and fourteen seals in its stomach.

HARBOR PORPOISE. In contrast to the dolphin, a porpoise has no beak-like profile and the back fin is more erect and triangular; porpoises are also smaller animals, rarely more than six feet in length. The back and the flippers are black, shading through gray on the sides to a white under surface. Each jaw bears about fifty small teeth. An Atlantic species ranges from Greenland to New Jersey, and a similar Pacific species from Alaska to California. Porpoises come to the surface several times a minute to breath, producing a hissing or sighing sound

Porpoise (*left*) and Dolphin (*right*).

well known to saltwater fishermen. Porpoises, like dolphins, feed on fish, squid, and small shellfish.

SPERM WHALE. This is the largest of our toothed cetaceans; it is also called the cachalot. Male sperm whales reach a length of sixty-five feet. Originally this giant mammal was common in both the Atlantic and Pacific oceans, but the whaling fleets have reduced the sperm-whale population so that today the species is found chiefly round Japan and Chile. The most famous whale in fiction is the albino individual immortalized as Moby Dick in Melville's story of the sea.

A sperm whale has a strange body form, quite different from the streamlined shape acquired by most marine mammals. The massive squared head extends about one third of the total length; a large portion of this is a skull cavity filled with spermaceti, an oily white substance formerly used in making candles. From the intestines of sick sperm whales comes a substance, ambergris, whose greasy grayish appearance belies the fact it is worth twenty dollars an ounce to the manufacturers of fine perfumes. One ship's crew found a 750-pound chunk of ambergris in the whale they had captured. However, the chief value of these big cetaceans has been the thick layer of blubber which was once in great demand as fuel for whale-oil lamps, before the discovery of petroleum. The blubber was also converted into candles, lubricating oil, cattle food, and fertilizer.

Sperm whales are uniform dark gray or bluish gray; they lack a back fin, and in its place have a series of low humps along the midline of the back. The narrow slender lower jaw is provided with many small teeth; the upper jaw is toothless. A single blowhole is located on the left front of the head. Sperm whales feed almost entirely on large squid and octopus as is evident from the numerous scars inflicted by the suckers of these animals. Sperm whales have a cruising speed of about six miles per hour, but when pursued they can double or triple this rate; they dive by raising their tails high and descending vertically, remaining submerged for as long as thirty minutes.

FINBACK WHALE.   The streamlined body of this whale is a contrast to the blunt-nosed and ponderous sperm whale; as its appearance indicates, it is a fast swimmer in spite of its seventy-foot-long bulk. The triangular back fin is located close to the tail. Although once found in all oceans, the finback is now not very common; a quarter of a million individuals were killed by whalers between 1900 and 1940. Like other toothless whales, the finback has two blowholes instead of the one found in the dolphins and sperm whale. Usually dark gray above, whitish underneath, this whale is also recognized by the numerous lengthwise furrows on the throat. Yellowish white whalebone hangs in sheets up to three feet long from the roof of the mouth. The finback cow usually has only a single calf, about twenty feet long at birth.

SULPHUR-BOTTOM WHALE.   The largest mammal which has ever lived, this unique species—also known as the blue whale—has joined the ranks of those unfortunate animals now practically extinct. Records indicate several specimens over 100 feet in length. An eighty-nine-foot individual with a forty-five foot girth weighed 119 tons. Such tremendous bulk can be supported only in a medium such as water; the extinct dinosaurs discovered this truth when it became a biological impossibility for their excessively large bodies to be supported by limbs. The summer home of this giant is in the ice-floes of the polar seas of both hemispheres. The body has a bluish tint, with mottled gray and white underparts including the furrowed throat. The name "sulphur-bottom" originated from the yellowish tint to the underside caused by a film of minute plants known as diatoms. The whalebone in this whale is bluish black. It is one of the curious quirks of nature that this hugest of all animals feeds on

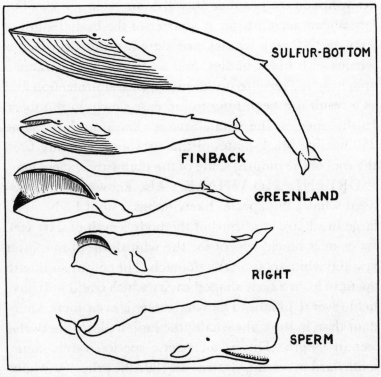

SULFUR-BOTTOM

FINBACK

GREENLAND

RIGHT

SPERM

Some Common Whales.

tiny shrimp-like midgets which are strained out of the water by the plates of whalebone. A newborn sulphur-bottom calf measures about twenty-five feet, and nurses until it is fifty-two feet long!

RIGHT WHALE. Because of its slow swimming speed and ease of capture, as well as the great yield of whale oil from its blubber, this was the "right" kind of whale for the whalers to pursue. Over a period of 700 years it was hunted along the seacoasts of northern Europe, Newfoundland, and New England. A right whale has no throat furrows and no back fin, but has enlarged fleshy lips on the peculiar outward-curved lower jaw. The large head accounts for a quarter of the body length of sixty feet. Right whales are slow-moving deep-water whales with black bodies; and seldom become stranded on a beach. They are under international protection and as a result are beginning to increase slowly in numbers. In this species, the whalebone is very abundant, some 250 flexible black plates of this substance hanging from the roof of the mouth; some of the plates are six feet long.

GREENLAND WHALE. Also known as the bowhead whale, this species likewise has a stout body and a large head, about a third of the body length of sixty feet. Its color is black, except for the whitish tip of the lower jaw and white spots on the stomach. The enormous mouth opens to form a boat-shaped cavity which could well have held several Jonahs. The whalebone is even more abundant than in the right whale; the largest plates are twelve feet in length. This is an Arctic species, rarely found southward in warmer waters. In 1897 the prices for whalebone were four dollars a pound, and whale oil sold for thirty cents a gallon. A single Greenland whale would net its captors 1500 pounds of whalebone and 80 barrels of oil, and thus provide $8000 profit to the owner of the ship and its crew. It is little wonder that in the early whaling days, many New England fortunes were built on these huge cetaceans.

THE MANATEE

Throughout the animal kingdom we find individual species which are so different from their relatives that they are placed in families or orders by themselves. Such an order is that of the *Sirenia* which includes two widely separated animals: the manatee or sea cow of Florida and the dugong of the Red Sea, Indian Ocean, and Australia. These peculiar mammals, ugly though they

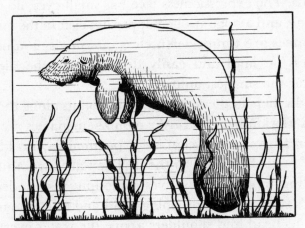

The favorite pose of the manatee, a rare aquatic mammal of Florida, is a floating position with arched body and drooping tail.

seem at close range, have sufficiently human traits to be credited with inspiring the mermaid myth. The ponderous animal has the habit of floating in an erect position, sometimes raising its head and shoulders out of the water; females, when nursing their young, clasp the babies to their breasts as they bob up and down on the water.

MANATEE. The manatee, which could well be named " the grazer of the sea" is a herbivor, lazily browsing on under-water grasses and weeds which it sweeps into its thick-lipped mouth with its flippers. This rare animal, found in a few locations along the south Florida coast, is dull gray, with hairless skin, a pair of pudgy forelimbs modified as paddles and no hindlimbs; the tail is horizontally flattened and used chiefly as a balancing organ. The favorite pose of a manatee is a semi-erect floating position with arched body and downward-curved tail. The ten- to twelve-foot-long body weighs up to 1000 pounds. The expressionless face has small eyes, no external ears, and a huge swollen upper lip, cleft in the middle. Manatees are timid, defenseless mammals, completely helpless on land and easily disturbed by the slightest noise or the smallest animal.

As dwellers in the semi-tropical habitats along the protected Florida bays and river mouths, manatees are delicate creatures very susceptible to pneumonia; a cold spell of 60°F. is often fatal to them. They are lazy animals, spending most of their lives in lolling just under the water's surface, with drooping head and tail. A manatee raises its head and shoulders above the water every five or ten minutes for several deep breaths. The baby manatee is born under water, and thus must swim at once; the mother bobs above the surface, however, when it is time to feed her young one, cradling it in her fleshy fore-limbs. The manatee is fully protected today, and thus is guaranteed survival in spite of man's invasion of its native habitat as his winter playground.

Little Brown Bat in Flight.

CHAPTER 6

SOME UNUSUAL MAMMALS

Nature often seems to delight in quirks of fancy, presenting us with strange survivors of ancient orders in otherwise highly specialized groups of animals, or with species which represent bold attempts at novel approaches to life. Among mammals we find many examples of this. One of these unique animals found within the United States is the opossum, descendant of one of the oldest families of mammals. Another is the armadillo, nature's experiment with body armor on a warm-blooded animal. Still another is the peccary, a native American wild pig. Mention of our unusual mammals must include two groups which have become highly specialized for environments ordinarily not occupied by fur-bearers: the moles, for completely subterranean living, and the bats for invasion of the realm of true flight.

OPOSSUM

Marsupials are mammals with primitive reproductive habits much less specialized than those of the mammals we have already considered. The young are born in an extremely undeveloped condition with only sufficient strength to crawl along the mother's abdomen into the safety of the marsupial pouch. Here the tiny babies remain until mature enough to venture out into the hostile world. Marsupials also have primitive tooth development and simple brains. The only representative of this order in the United States is the opossum.

OPOSSUM. The 'possum is ordinarily thought of as a southern mammal, for its original range extended from Texas to Florida, northward to Virginia. However in recent years, aided perhaps by a succession of mild winters, the 'possum has spread to New England and New York, west to the Great Lakes states. In spite of its primitive characteristics, it is such a hardy and adaptable animal that it seems to have no difficulty in competing on its home ground with many of its more highly specialized mammal relatives.

An opossum is hardly a beautiful animal. The pointed yellowish face, framed by naked black ears, has a mouth often partly open in a snarling fashion showing numerous small teeth. The rather unkempt fur coat of coarse guard hairs, over the shorter underfur, contains some black hairs and some white. The black hairs are shorter than the white ones, resulting in a grizzled grayish coat of nondescript color. The naked, scaly tail is very long and prehensile like that of some monkeys. An average indi-

Opossum. The baby 'possum is smaller than a bee.

vidual is two and a half feet in length, and weighs ten pounds. The flesh is considered tasty especially in the South where the 'possum is hunted a great deal; it is also trapped for the fur, used in trimming coats.

Even though the 'possum is an expert climber, it is as much at home on the ground as in trees. The forefoot is armed with five clawed toes which are an aid in climbing; the big toe of the hindfoot can be opposed to the other digits, a very useful feature in clasping branches. A 'possum has a fifth "foot" in the guise of the long muscular tail; this can be curled around a branch for support or used to carry grasses for the nest. Most active at night, opossums forage for ants, grasshoppers, crickets, and other delectable insects. If these are not available, they devour anything that is edible: worms, mice, small reptiles and amphibians, fruits, berries, and carrion. In recent years 'possums have become bold enough to raid refuse cans in suburban backyards. By fall they become very fat; so they can indulge during cold spells in long periods of sleep, wrapped in leaves in a cozy underground burrow or hollow tree.

This peculiar mammal is well known for its habit of feigning death, or "playing 'possum." The excitement of being attacked or pursued throws the animal into a state of nervous shock; it becomes paralyzed with fear and falls into a limp heap, usually on its side, with eyes closed and tongue hanging out of its mouth. As soon as the danger has passed, the 'possum miraculously recovers and takes off with great speed. This behavior may be of some survival value since many carnivors will not eat a dead animal.

Before the baby opossums are born, the mother prepares a nest of dried vegetation in a hollow tree or hole in the ground. She carries the nest-building material in a unique fashion, placing the grass and twigs first in her mouth and then tucking it by means of her forefeet into a coil of the tail, held under the body. About a dozen very tiny babies are born at one time, each the size of a bumblebee; all could easily be carried in a tablespoon. As soon as a 'possum is born it pulls itself by its strong forelimbs through the dense jungle of the mother's hair and by instinct (for it is blind) finds the opening to her pouch. Crawling in, it fastens itself to a teat where it remains securely attached for weeks. Since there are only thirteen of these milk-dispensers, if more than this number of brothers and sisters occur in a litter, the last to reach the food supply of necessity die. A 'possum can have two or three litters a year. Such large families are one reason for the spread of these mammals throughout the

East. They have also become introduced and established in the Pacific coast states.

ARMADILLO

The Edentates are peculiar mammals which have degenerated to a toothless, or nearly toothless, condition and so have to rely upon small prey such as insects for sustenance. The group includes the anteaters and sloths, both furred mammals. The representative in our country is the armadillo. This strange animal has about thirty small teeth but all are premolars or molars; its long sticky tongue darts back and forth over the ground, sweeping up countless numbers of ants, ant eggs, and other insects and their larvae.

ARMADILLO.   An armored tank among mammals, this animal seems a strange combination of turtle and pig. No one would have any difficulty in recognizing this yellowish brown animal protected by a shell instead of a fur coat. The back is overlaid by nine curved bands of bony plates, extending crosswise of the body. The top of

Armadillo. Baby armadillos are generally born as quadruplets.

the head and also the tail are protected by a shell-like covering. Between the plates of bone grow small coarse hairs; the sparse hairy feature is most evident on the unprotected abdomen. This armor serves as excellent protection against enemies likely to pounce on its back, and also against the thorny underbrush into which the animal darts when pursued.

Armadillos are very numerous south of the Rio Grande River; until fifty or sixty years ago these mammals were unknown except in southern Texas. Man has very obligingly reduced the numbers of their enemies among the carnivors so that today the armadillo has spread into Oklahoma, Louisiana, and Arkansas. It appeared east of the Mississippi River even before bridges were built, and escaped individuals have established themselves in Florida. Since these warm-blooded animals cannot hibernate, prolonged cold spells are fatal to them. With this handicap, biologists believe that the armadillo has now reached the northernmost limit of its possible range.

An armadillo is the size of a large housecat, with a length of two or two and a half feet, weighing about fifteen pounds. The pointed pig-like snout is used for plowing through leaf mold in search of insects and grubs. The stocky body is supported by short limbs; the forefeet have strong long claws which are excellent digging tools. Armadillos are very near-sighted and have poor hearing. They are sensitive to ground vibrations, however, and take off for the shelter of a cactus thicket or mesquite clump when approached. Armadillos move in a nervous, jerky fashion as they shuffle along with their noses in the earth. They dislike heat, in summer staying below ground or in a cave during most of the daytime hours. It is surprising how well this clumsy armored animal swims; gulping in air to keep from sinking, it moves through the water with short fast strokes. At other times armadillos will hold their breath, and cross small streams by walking along the bottom, on the stream bed.

An armadillo may dig an underground den, or occupy a small cave or crevice in the limestone outcrops which form its preferred habitat. The female gives birth to identical quadruplets, which arrive in March or April. Baby armadillos have soft, leathery plates which gradually toughen but do not become completely hard until adult size is reached. This temporary flexibility is necessary; for armadillos do not molt like crabs, and once the shell is rigidly set, the body within cannot increase in size. The flesh of armadillo is very tasty, especially when barbecued with a hot sauce as is often done in Texas where it goes by the name of "poor man's pig." Armadillos make unusual and interesting pets, but will not live long if kept in a cage.

PECCARY

The American Indians who lived here before the coming of the white man had only two domesticated animals, the dog and the turkey. Our domesticated hoofed animals—horses, cattle, sheep, goats, and pigs—are all descendants of species brought into the United States by the early Spanish and English explorers. Yet we have several native species which are close relatives of these introduced hoofed mammals. Wild cattle are represented by the buffalo; wild sheep, by the bighorn; and wild goats, by the mountain goat. A lone representative of the wild pigs is the peccary or javelina, common in Mexico and found north of the Rio Grande River in Texas, New Mexico, and Arizona.

PECCARY. About fifty thousand of these strange little wild pigs are left in the Southwest today, whereas formerly they were much more abundant and ranged northward into Arkansas. Unrestricted hunting has reduced the population to its present numbers. The peccary is a stocky animal with a pig-like snout, thick neck, arched back, an erectile mane, short legs, and very short tail. The fur coat, of long coarse hair, is grizzled brownish gray. On the front feet are four toes; the two with hoofs touch the ground, the other two are dewclaws and do not reach that far. The hindfeet have two hoofed toes and one dewclaw far up on the leg. The upper canine teeth are large and pointed, resembling small tusks. An average individual is three feet in length and weighs forty-five pounds.

Peccaries are nervously active animals, scooting about under mesquite and other desert plants, grunting and yapping as they plow up the ground with their snouts, uncovering edible roots and tubers, nuts, acorns, and occasional toads or turtle eggs. Other animals of the arid Southwest have learned to do without water, but the peccary has not. In their search for water, bands of these animals congregate around waterholes, tramping the moist soil with hundreds of small hoof marks. Twins are born to the female peccary during any of the summer months, usually in a hollow log or burrow. The babies are reddish brown mixed with black; when captured young, they are said to make good pets. Man hunts the peccary for its flesh, which, however, is too tough and dry for the average taste. Other enemies of the peccary are the jaguar, ocelot, and coyote. When cornered a peccary fights gamely and savagely, taking care to keep its back protected by a rock or tree. A musk gland on the back, near the tail, leaves a strong odor which often is the only indication of the presence of these unusual wild pigs.

MOLES

Among the rodents, many species (woodchuck, prairie dog, gopher) have retreated into the ground and as a result have become modified for subterranean living, though they still spend considerable time above ground. Among the insectivors the moles are excellent examples of mammals which have practically given up an above-ground existence, to become completely adapted for underground life. Although there are about forty kinds of moles in the United States, the uniformity of living conditions beneath the surface of the earth has made them all look very much alike.

A mole's body is cylindrical with few external projections to offer resistance in moving through small tunnels or burrows. The fur is short and velvety, and external ears have disappeared. Shoulders and forelimbs are heavy and muscular, and the broad feet and claws act as efficient shovels: these are the excavating equipment of this living bulldozer. The hindlimbs and feet are small, the tail is short. Since eyes are of little use to an animal which spends all or most of its life in the dark, some moles are completely blind, with eyelids grown over useless eyeballs, while other moles have tiny eyes and can see objects close by. When these moles come above ground occasionally, they avoid bright light and scurry under the shade of grasses and woodland litter. Like other insectivors, moles have numerous small primitive teeth. The nose is an especially sensitive part of the body, with numerous nerve endings; it is used in deciding where its prey is located, and where to dig.

Most people have never seen a live mole, but they are familiar with the raised ridges which disfigure their lawns. Moles dig two kinds of tunnels. The one near the surface, which is revealed by the meandering ridges, is a feeding passageway dug for the purpose of getting food. Moles have big appetites, and eat two-thirds of their weight each day. They live almost entirely on worms, grubs, insects, and other small invertebrates found in the upper layers of the soil. Destruction of flower bulbs and roots are incidental casualties of the mole's search for animal food; it does not eat them. Moles are active day and night, the year round. They can dig feeding tunnels at the rate of twelve feet an hour, and may never return to use the passage again. A mole pushing ahead into the soft soil with its pointed snout shovels the dirt to either side by means of its shovel-like paws, then pushes the soil upward with its strong shoulders in order to make room for the tunnel; it is this raised soil which forms the ridge. A mole has an uncanny sense of direction in relation to the contour of the land keeping the same distance beneath the surface and rarely breaking through.

The deeper tunnels are used as living quarters and winter retreats; moles are unsociable animals, each usually having its own tunnel system and living alone. In digging the deeper passages, the mole must get rid of the excavated material. To do this, it digs a vertical shaft every few feet and carries the earth to the surface. These piles of excavated dirt are the familiar molehills left by some kinds of moles. In the deeper tunnels the female has her babies, one litter of several young a year. Adult moles have few enemies when they stay underground. On the surface they are snatched up by hawks, owls, and the smaller carnivors. In spite of their occasional damage to lawns, moles are valuable assets because of their role in consuming quantities of grubs and insects injurious to it and in aerating and enriching the soil.

COMMON EASTERN MOLE. This mole is blind, for the eyes are covered with skin; the pointed snout is naked at the tip. Its fur coat is a soft grayish or brownish color, but is not of sufficient value to be sought by trappers. Commercial mole fur comes from Canada and Great Britain. This species of mole grows to a length of eight inches, and weighs two ounces. It is found from southern New England and New York to Minnesota and southward to Florida and Texas. It rarely leaves molehills as evidence of its presence. A related eastern species, the HAIRY-TAILED MOLE, is not entirely blind, but has well-hidden small eyes. It ranges farther north and east, beyond the Canadian border. The hairy-tailed mole leaves no molehills as it digs its deep tunnels to get below the frost line.

STAR-NOSED MOLE. The star-nosed mole has a pointed snout terminating in an unusual rosette of some twenty fleshy rays or tentacles; when searching for food, the fleshy rays are in constant motion and seem to act as sensory organs. This mole is found from Canada and New England westward to the Great Lakes and south to the Carolinas. The fur coat is a glossy brown or black. Star-nosed moles have small eyes and are the same length and weight as the common eastern mole. They prefer damp meadows and woods, or swamps, since they like to be near water. They forage for earthworms, crayfish, and other aquatic invertebrates, much of the food being grubbed from the debris at the bottom of ponds. The star-nosed mole swims well and often can be seen moving beneath the ice in winter; at this season it will tunnel through the snow. The young are born in an underground nest, in May or June.

WESTERN MOLE. Native to Washington, Oregon, and California, this western species resembles the common eastern mole except for its larger size; it grows to a length of nine inches. The western mole is also blind, for its eyes are buried beneath the skin. It leaves numerous molehills, about three feet apart, as evidence of its digging. Western moles live in open valleys, meadows, or forests. Their black silky fur is the most prized of all our native moles.

BATS

Mammals have not been satisfied with colonizing every available niche on the surface of the land, in its depths, and in the waters which cover so much of the earth. They have also ventured into the air, achieving true flight and thus competing with the birds. Bats are the only mammals which can fly.

Superficially bats resemble birds, for both have wings. However the wings of a bird and those of a bat differ greatly since they did not originate in the same way. Both are highly specialized forelimbs, but there the similarity stops. In present-day birds, the arm bone and forearm bone form the supporting framework of the wing; the fingers (there are only three) are small and of little value in the wing structure, and do not terminate in claws. In bats, the arm and forearm bones are less important as support for the wing whose main framework consists of extremely long fingers; the thumb is free, ending in a claw. The wing of a bat extends between the fingers and from the fifth digit to the body and hindlimb. Another obvious difference between a bat and a bird is that the supporting surface of a bird's wing is overlapping feathers; that of a bat's, thin leathery skin. A bat has the advantage of a claw on each wing, which can be used in climbing, but is at a disadvantage by having the hindlimbs also attached to the wings. Thus a bat has difficulty in traveling on the ground; the greatest use of the clawed hindfeet is in hanging upside down when the animal is asleep.

Bats have varying flying techniques. One kind of bat flies with short swift strokes of its wings, like a bird. Another kind flies erratically, twisting and dodging and changing its course continually. Still another flies irregularly and flutters like a huge butterfly. The insectivorous diet of the bat accounts partly for its erratic flight; the bat catches its meal on the wing, pursuing flying insects in the air and having to dart wherever the insects happen to be. The bat's type of flight is also due to the fact that these flying mammals do not depend upon eyesight but upon a special sense similar to radar. Bats are not blind, as is popularly believed; they have small eyes, capable of limited vision. But they depend upon their remarkable ability to send out sound vibrations which bounce back from objects and are received by special sensory organs; thus a bat has both a transmitting and a receiving set for judging distance. These echo-producing sounds cannot be heard by the human ear; for they are of extremely high frequency, some in the range of fifty kilocycles. Bats are constantly sending out these supersonic vibrations, and use the echo, or returning vibration as a guide to their flight.

The bat has a mouse-like body with large ears combined peculiarly with the head of a miniature bulldog. In some languages the bat is known as a "flying mouse" or "flying fox," we have a species called the mastiff bat. Most bats weigh only a fraction of an ounce, in spite of their fur making them appear larger. They sleep through the days, hanging upside down, in hollow trees, abandoned buildings, and caves. At dusk they become active in search for insects.

A most memorable sight is the regular evening exodus of Mexican free-tailed bats from Carlsbad Caverns, in the New Mexico national park of the same name. During the day millions of these bats hang on the walls and ceilings of a huge room in the Caverns, a quarter of a mile long and over a hundred feet high. After sunset, as the air currents in the caverns change, a muffled roar like the sound of surf at a great distance can be heard at the cavern mouth as the bats awaken and begin streaming out into the night. The bats are so close to each other as they emerge that they resemble a cloud of smoke pouring out of the huge hole in the cactus-studded cliffs. The procession continues for fifteen or twenty minutes. Hours later, before sunrise, the movement is reversed and the cloud of bats funnels back into the caverns. On each of these nightly forays it is estimated that the bats consume many tons of injurious insects.

It was the phenomenon of this flight of bats which led

to the discovery and exploration of the Carlsbad Caverns. Jim White, a cowboy on the lookout for guano, the rich deposit of bat excreta, traced the bats into the caverns and found plenty of it. At one time guano sold for ninety dollars a ton. When the size and beauty of the caverns became fully known procuring guano became secondary to the protection of these amazing caverns as a national park. A visit to this park is not complete without being on hand to see the nightly parade of these flying mammals.

Mother bats usually give birth to a single baby. The mother hangs by her feet and thumbs, spreading her body and wings as an apron into which the baby is born. The blind, naked young bat is held in the mother's folded wings during the day; when she flies out at night she carries the baby with her, clinging to her body. When two weeks old, the young bats are left behind hanging in the "dormitory" by themselves; at three weeks they start flying and catch their own meals. Bats have few enemies, so, unlike most wild animals, many bats may die of old age; their estimated life span is ten years. Accidental death comes to many through wind and hail storms, and in unusually cold spells and heavy snows. Some bats migrate to warmer regions during winter, others hibernate in the constant temperature of caverns where the thermometer stays between 34° and 40°F. While hibernating they breathe about once every five minutes, and their body temperatures drop to that of their environment.

LITTLE BROWN BAT. The little brown bat is the most common of our native bats. It can be recognized by the lack of fur on the membrane between the tail and the hindlimbs. The body is covered with reddish

– 167 –

brown or black close fur, and is three to four inches in length. Little brown bats are found in every state, and extend into Canada to the northern limit of tree growth. In addition to their ultrasonic sounds, the little brown bat, like other bats, utters a variety of soft calls, squeaks, buzzes and clicking sounds. Neither this species nor any other deliberately tries to get into human's hair; it is very rare for a bat to collide with a person.

PIPISTRELLE. The pipistrelles are our smallest bats, with a length of three inches and only a five-inch wingspread. The fur is smoky gray or brown. They occur in the eastern half of the United States, and in the Southwest. Pipistrelles have the habit of emerging from their hiding places at dusk, feeding for a few hours, retiring for a rest, and then reappearing just before dawn for another short foray for insects.

BIG BROWN BAT. Sooty to pale brown in color, the big brown bat, as its name implies, has a large body, up to five inches in length, and a wingspread of a foot. This is the bat which commonly winters in dwellings, barns, and church steeples. It is found throughout the United States. The size and color are distinctive, as well as the long, loose fur.

RED BAT. The upper surface of the membrane between the tail and the hindlimbs of the red bat is covered with fur; this is reddish brown as is all its fur, and soft as plush. The presence of whitish hair tips gives the coat a frosted appearance. A red bat measures about four inches in length but has a wingspread of thirteen inches. It is found throughout the eastern two-thirds of the United States. Unlike many other bats, it does not hibernate but migrates southward in winter, northward in summer. Red bats have been known to travel as far as Bermuda. They fly swiftly, and may even alight on trees and bushes to catch their insect prey.

FREE-TAILED BAT. As its name suggests the free-tailed bat has a tail which extends beyond the membrane connecting the hindlimb with the body. It is a brownish or smoky bat, three to four inches in length. The wings are narrow and the body is relatively large. Free-tailed bats take no long migrations, and rarely hibernate all winter. The flying insects which make up their diet include beetles and moths. In addition to being the bat which makes Carlsbad Caverns famous, this species is the common house bat of the Southwest.

The young of the Rocky Mountain goat, like all baby mammals, are extremely curious.

CHAPTER SEVEN

MAMMALS AT HOME

For many years, in our new country, biologists were kept busy identifying the many different species of mammals, determining their geographic distribution, and their economic importance to man. In recent years the attention of mammalogists has centered more on the behavior of mammals, the peculiarities of mammal populations, and the family life of our fur-bearing friends. Gradually we are learning that the individual mammal has a distinctive personality and an ability to solve, on an elementary level, many problems of daily living in much the same way as we do. Thus we can picture the mammal as a home-builder and architect, as a parent and family provider, and as an ingenious innovator when it comes to avoiding the hardships of winter.

When a nature walk takes us through fields where we spy a vigilant woodchuck or glimpse the shadowy form of a fox, or through woods where we surprise some chattering squirrels on a tree stump or a porcupine clambering into the upper branches of a sapling, we rarely think of these animals as being *at home*. Yet actually that is just where they are. Most animals have a very restricted area where they spend their entire lives; in this little domain each one knows where to find its food, where to escape its enemies, where to find the trail to its sleeping quarters. This area is known as the individual's home range. The home range of most mammals is surprisingly small. Studies of the brown rat show that its home area has a diameter of less than a hundred feet; the home range of other small mammals is from a fraction of an acre to several acres. Larger animals, since they need more food, require a bigger home range; if carnivors, one of several square miles. Desert areas can support only a few individuals per square mile as compared with dense forests; hence a desert home range is usually much larger than one in the fertile plains and woodlands. A large carnivor such as the bear may have a home extending ten miles in any direction from its den; wolves in the far North are known to need an area of some hundred square miles.

Within this range, an individual will tolerate other individuals of the same species, but the total population will depend upon the available food supply. Biologists have studied this aspect of the lives of our game animals and, as a result, know exactly the maximum number of deer or elk or mountain lions which can survive in a given game refuge. It is one of the basic rules of wild-life conservation to maintain this normal balance. Mammals lay out specific landmarks in their home range, known as signposts. These may be claw or antler marks on a tree, odor trails or other signs of mammal presence. They have a network of trails and hidden pathways, places where they sun themselves, places where they wallow or bathe, places where they play, and places where they sleep. The individual is very comfortable in this area; for it knows that, if caught by surprise, it can quickly find its way to a safe spot. An animal taken from its home range and released elsewhere requires a much longer time to find a hiding spot, discover food, and otherwise adjust to the new environment.

With this intimate knowledge of every inch of its home range, the mammal's first reaction to surprise by an enemy is usually flight. This impulse makes it difficult for the average pedestrian, noisily making his way along a wooded trail, to see many mammals; they have fled to safety at the first sound of human footsteps. If a mammal is caught by surprise and considers flight impossible, its usual secondary defense is to lie absolutely still. Most species, and especially the young, are so protectively marked that they blend into the surroundings. How often we can trace the course of a rabbit when it is in motion, but when it "freezes" and flattens itself against the ground, how rarely can we find it at all. If neither flight nor lying motionless are of use, even the smallest mammal will fight with whatever weapons it is endowed, biting ferociously and using claws as effectively as teeth in self-defense. Hoofs and horns make sharp spears and daggers, although their development was not primarily for this purpose. On the other hand, even huge carnivors rarely attack man with no reason. The most notable example of a mammal which will go out of its way to pick a fight with man is a mother while nursing or bringing up her young. A she-bear with cubs is a dangerous subject for close-up photography.

THE HOMES OF MAMMALS

Mammals are much like people. Some are nomads, restlessly wandering over their home range, careless about where they sleep and seemingly either uninterested in the need for a permanent home or unwilling to labor to construct one. The hoofed mammals and most of the large carnivors are of this nomadic disposition. Then there are the apartment-house dwellers which will "rent" any kind of dwelling vacated by another mammal; they are usually too lazy to make their homes, but will gladly take over and even modify the dwellings constructed by more industrious tenants. Some members of the dog family and many rodents have this habit. Finally there are the true home-builders, with an overpowering desire for a place of their own, constructed by their own labor according to their own blueprints. Some of these build nests, others excavate complicated underground dwellings, and still others build impressive lodges. Be it an adopted shack or a carefully constructed palace, home is where the mammal goes to sleep and rest, to escape unfavorable weather, to elude its enemies, to hoard its food, and to raise its family. When near its home, the animal considers the area immediately adjacent its special territory and drives away any other individual even of the same species. It is belligerent in this home territory, and ready to fight to the death any intruder. Thus our human idea that a home is a man's castle has its parallel in the home-building instinct of some mammals.

Many species are satisfied with any handy opening in the ground, hole in a rotting log, or crevice in a rock pile, as a home. The small carnivors generally appropriate a hole in a bank or a runway between rocks as a snug retreat, hauling dried leaves and grasses to make the bedroom comfortable and help the sleeping animal retain its body heat. But other mammal species are more fussy, constructing such a variety of homes as nests, burrows, and lodges.

The tree squirrels are great nest builders. Their often clumsy and ponderous nests are conspicuous in the higher branches of nut trees in winter, when the trees are leafless. A suitable location of forking limbs or tangle of branches is selected for a support on which to build. Using both forepaws and teeth, the squirrel weaves bits of grass, leaves, twigs, and bark into a roughly spherical nest some sixteen to twenty inches in diameter. Inside, the coarse walls are lined with softer plant materials, making a single room, windproof and dry, about four inches in diameter. Usually a single opening, on the side, acts as the entrance. Winter rains and snows freeze onto the outside of this crude nest and add to the weatherproofing of the home in the tree-tops. Some squirrels add a touch of interior decorating by hanging a drapery of moss or lichens over the doorway, which is pushed aside as the occupant enters or leaves.

The red squirrel is not satisfied with one home. It may have a nest, but also sets up a bedroom in a tree hollow or bank crevice. Occasionally a red squirrel will try to excavate a burrow, but rarely does more than create a dugout about nine inches in diameter, which it fills with shredded bark and soft leaves. The large fox squirrel is a wealthy home-owner with summer and winter residences. The summer nest is a hastily constructed affair of branches and leaves, in a tree near its favorite feeding ground. If the nest falls to pieces in a few weeks, the squirrel may build another "shanty" for summer use. However the winter nest is a carefully built home, capable of lasting several years. The outer shell, built on an aerial platform, is made of twigs with leaves attached, laced into a rough wall. Then the builder presses layers of damp leaves on the inside, as we plaster a wall. Finally the nest is lined with the softest bits of bark and leaves the squirrel can find.

A few rodents have learned to build aerial nests similar to those of birds; such nests are built by harvest mice, cotton rats, rice rats, and at times by white-footed mice and jumping mice. The harvest mouse builds its nest among the grasses and weeds, sometimes near the ground but at other times higher in the bushes. The tiny architect begins its home-building by gathering sections of grass and weaving them firmly to a supporting stem or twig; gradually a cup-shaped structure is formed and finally a roof is added which eventually arches over the entire nest. The mouse moves its feet and teeth with remarkable speed in intertwining the building materials. The reward of its industry is a snug home the size and shape of a grapefruit, with an opening about half an inch in diameter as an entrance. The interior is lined with such soft material as cattail floss and milkweed down. All mammal nest-builders seem to like comfort as well as the more essential and practical features of a home.

The ideal location for a safe home, warm in winter and air-conditioned in summer, is underground. But not all mammals have the digging equipment and the know-how to construct such a home. It is among the rodents, with their chisel-like teeth and strong claws, short limbs and compact muscular bodies, that we find the best builders of underground homes.

The friendly woodchuck selects any meadow, field, or hillside with loose well-drained soil as a home site, especially if it is near a choice food supply such as an apple orchard or a farmer's vegetable garden. The front door may be hidden under bushes or an overhanging rock, or may be in plain sight; in all cases it is marked by the large mound of excavated dirt brought to the surface by the woodchuck. Inside the entrance, the hallway, which starts out about a foot in diameter, narrows to half that width and extends gradually downward for ten or twenty feet; enlarged spaces along the way provide places where the bulky animal can turn around. Two to six feet below the surface, the hallway forks and numerous passageways lead to other enlarged areas and rooms. One or two bedrooms are located far back at the end of a main

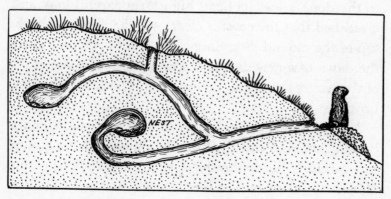

Woodchuck Burrow.

passageway. The bedroom is about a foot and a half in diameter and ten inches high; grass and leaves hauled in by the woodchuck provide comfortable bedding. Often the location of the bedroom shows some foresight, for it is higher than the middle portion of the hallways, thus eliminating the danger of being flooded. Other smaller rooms serve as toilets; the woodchuck is a clean house-keeper, and if it cannot go out of doors, it uses a special room for this purpose, filling it with earth when it can no longer be used.

Mammals living underground must be able to outwit enemies which may follow them into their burrows. The woodchuck, for example, has several emergency exits at the end of various hallways. These are dug from within and have no telltale external mounds; the openings are often hidden in bushes. A steep inclined passageway leads to each of these exits. The woodchuck retreats to its home every night. Before leaving in the morning, it waddles to a point a few feet inside the entrance and pauses to listen. It may whistle a low note, or give a wavering call. If everything remains quiet, the woodchuck slowly comes to the door, sticks its head high for a careful look and, if satisfied that the coast is clear, will then proceed to the top of the mound. Standing erect, the woodchuck greets the dawn of a new day, and with these preliminaries out of the way, proceeds to the important business of finding breakfast.

A kangaroo rat shows great individuality in its home-building. Some locate the front door flush with the ground but carefully hidden under a protecting rock or clump of bushes. Others build a large mound first, some mounds being sixteen feet in diameter and four feet high. In the mound may be as many as a dozen doors, each opening into a maze of hallways. The mound-builders are at an advantage in flat country subject to floods, for their entrances remain dry. Generations of kangaroo rats may occupy one home, and as a result the architecture is constantly subject to change as remodeling goes on. The front hallway leads to passageways which may extend as ramps up and down to three or four living levels. These interior passageways are three or four inches in diameter. Some rooms which open off the passageways are pantries and storerooms, filled with the kangaroo rat's favorite foods for winter use; these are generally in the driest part of the building. At the far end of the deepest passageway is a bedroom bedded with grass and leaves. An untidy housekeeper, this rat has no rooms set aside as toilets and so the passageways and bedrooms are not as clean as those of the woodchuck.

Pocket gophers are burrowing rodents which spend so much of their time underground that they devote more energy to making their living quarters comfortable than animals which simply sleep or hibernate in an underground home. Each animal designs and constructs its own home and prefers to live in it as a hermit. The entrance and hallways are only two or three inches in diameter. Instead of dumping all the excavated material at the entrance, the pocket gopher breaks through vertically at intervals along the tunnel, spreads the excavated dirt fanwise, and plugs up the opening from within. A maze of upper hallways, near the surface, are feeding galleries where succulent bulbs and roots abound. Small rooms off these passageways act as storerooms and are filled with grass cuttings, bulbs, and other edible plant parts. A sharply descending hallway leads to lower levels where the living quarters are located, perhaps ten feet below the surface. A spherical room, filled with shredded grass and leaves, is the pocket gopher's bedroom; some food may be stored here also. Nearby is a smaller room which is used as a toilet, and filled with dirt when it becomes necessary to use another room for this purpose. All in all, if one has to stay underground most of one's life, this is a cozy home with all the essentials provided for.

The most elaborate home of any underground mammal is that of the prairie dog. Being sociable animals, prairie dogs like to build their homes close together and thus large communities develop, spreading over many miles. The individual prairie dog starts its home with an entrance about six or eight inches in diameter. This

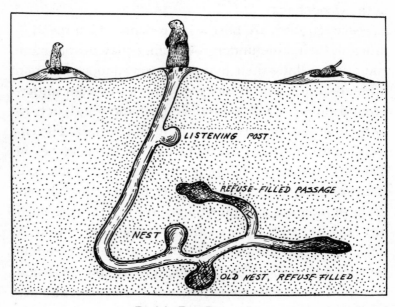

Prairie Dog Burrow.

opens onto a downward sloping ramp which functions as the main hallway and extends to depths of three to eighteen feet, depending upon the firmness of the soil and the depth of the water table. Prairie dogs which live on high sloping ground dump the excavated dirt in a haphazard fashion outside the front door. The prairie dog of the plains states lives on flat, often low, ground which is easily flooded by sudden cloudbursts; by sad experience, undoubtedly, prairie dogs in such locations have learned the value of building a dike around the opening into their home. The excavated dirt is built into a crater-like mound several feet high, completely encircling the front door. In times of flood, water can cover the ground to a depth of a foot or two and yet, by constructing this type of mound, the prairie dog has kept its home dry.

A few feet within the entrance hallway the prairie dog digs out a small side chamber which serves as a guard room or listening post. Before venturing out into the upper world, the occupant pauses here to be sure it is safe to go farther. Beyond the guard room the hallway often turns upward and wanders with many loops and blind passages. In some homes there is an emergency exit, or back door, used also as a means of getting excavated material out of the burrow. Along the main hallway, or at its end, is a round bedroom, eight to ten inches in diameter; this is lined with bedding material of dried grass and stems. Some of the more fastidious prairie-dog homes have special bathrooms, as in the homes of a few other rodents.

The construction of an above-ground lodge requires the skill of a carpenter and wood-cutter more than that of a miner. Such structures are built by wood rats, muskrats, and beavers. The wood rat, or pack rat, begins its home with the customary spherical nest of woven grasses and bark, about ten inches in diameter, with a small entrance at the side or the top. But this species seems to like to putter and change the architecture of its woody nest just for the fun of doing something. Soon an impregnable fortress is built by piling sticks and rubble crisscross around and over the nest and along the trails leading to the doorway. This massive dwelling may be on the ground, or in the branches of a tree or shrub. The clumsy piles of branches may be five or six feet in diameter and several feet in height. In the Southwest the pack rat cleverly lines the entrance trail with spiny sections of cholla cactus and other thorny shrubs which discourage other animals from intruding. Within the pile of woody debris the rat has several rooms, one of which may be a listening post, another a bedroom. The whole lodge may be chinked with leaves and earth to make it weathertight. Storerooms are an important part of this architect's design, though some are merely enlarged portions of the hallways. They are filled with pinon seeds, nuts, acorns, mesquite beans, and other desert delicacies for winter use. In addition, all the strange useless objects collected by this fascinating rodent add decorative touches to the interior of its home.

Muskrats have several types of homes. A favorite is a den in a stream bank, whose entrance is tunneled beneath the water level but with living quarters at a higher level, close to the surface of the ground. In the bedroom, which is about eight inches in diameter and six inches high, the muskrat piles sections of cattails and rushes to make a bed. It is a slightly damp room, since this material has had to be carried underwater and then up into the bedroom; but since the muskrat itself is always dripping wet when it enters its home, it may not notice this condition. Sometimes a second passageway and emergency exit is excavated. A nearby spot is used for an outside toilet, so that bedroom and living quarters remain quite clean.

At other times a muskrat may build itself a lodge in a suitable pond or slow-moving stream; its foundation is often a small island or pile of vegetation. Wigwam-shaped at first, the lodge is made of sticks but, as material is added year by year, a rounded structure develops. This may be three or four feet high if occupied by a single individual. Large community lodges have been found which are twenty feet long and three feet high, above water level. An underwater entrance leads into a central, rather austere chamber which serves as the combined livingroom and bedroom. In winter the exterior freezes into a protective outer wall.

For centuries man has marveled at the architectural skill, engineering ability, and industry of the beaver. The beaver can lay claim to being the world's first engineer; while our cave-dwelling ancestors were still living in any natural opening provided by nature, these animals were skillfully taking natural materials and fabricating them into dams and homes. A beaver always carries along the tools of its trade: the chisel-like teeth, strong claws, and muscular limbs. They provide the equipment to cut down building materials, transport them to the site where the dam is being built or the home constructed, and fashion them into a planned design. A beaver can cut down a five-inch willow tree in a few minutes; though it takes longer, a beaver of champion strength can cut through a tree four feet in diameter. The tree-cutting is done methodically as the beaver squats on its hind legs and tail, cutting an upper notch, then a lower one, and finally tearing out the intervening chip. When the tree starts swaying, the beaver scurries to a safe spot; after the crash, it waits to see if the noise has attracted any enemies. If not, the animal returns, cuts the trunk and limbs into convenient lengths for hauling, grips one end of a cut section in its teeth and drags it to the water. Here the going is easier, and the beaver swims alongside, towing the log to its destination.

When the trees near the water have been used up, the beaver has to venture farther inland for its building materials. Now the beaver becomes a navigation engineer

A tree cut down by a beaver shows clean-cut marks as if felled by a woodsman's axe.

and digs a canal in which it can float the logs to the home site. In some cases these remarkable animals have even built locks in the canals to lessen their transportation labor. Such canals are often of great length; instances of these canals six- and seven-hundred feet long have been discovered.

Some beavers, living by ponds and streams without a fluctuating water level, have no need of either dams or lodges; these live in dens dug in the banks. An essential of beaver house planning is to have the entrance underwater, but the living quarters above water. This means that if the home site is in a stream too shallow at low water for such an entrance, a dam has to be built which will keep the water at a minimum level. This dam and the lodge it provides for are built by the "lodge beavers." A beaver begins its dam by heaping driftwood, logs it has cut, mud, and stones across the stream. On the downstream face of the foundation material the beaver lays rows of logs, parallel to the stream direction, and weighted with mud and stones. On the upstream side the beaver plasters more mud, debris, and wet leaves. Soon most of the leaks are stopped, and the water level has risen, creating an artificial pond. The longest beaver dam on record was one discovered in Montana, almost half a mile in length; such large dams are undoubtedly the work of many generations of beavers. The average dam is five feet high and a few hundred feet in length. They are built so sturdily that a man can walk across them in safety.

Near the deepest spot in the beaver's artificial pond is the lodge; this often is built on a small island or on a mass of vegetation. Sticks are dragged to the spot and

A beaver dam and lodge are monuments to the industry and engineering ability of this mammal.

laid in a fashion to construct a circular structure, with several doorways leading into the water. Stones, mud, leaves, logs are piled to form a wall several feet high; then the material added is built inward to form an arching roof. The finishing touches, in the form of a plaster made of mud, are applied by the beaver as it carries armfuls of mud while walking erect and steadying itself by the muscular tail. A lodge is usually about seven feet high and thirty feet in diameter, with a single living-bedroom about three or four feet in diameter. A pioneer tale relates how one John Colter, noted for exploring the Yellowstone country, escaped from pursuing Indians by diving into a beaver pond and hiding inside the lodge. A lodge may be the home of one beaver, but more commonly it houses several families, the group living and working together harmoniously. Grownups sleep on the floor, but the baby beavers are provided with soft mattresses of dried vegetation. In the northern states, beavers would starve during winter if they left their food supplies of fresh-cut logs on the banks. Therefore they spend a busy autumn sinking log sections underwater so that they will remain below the ice. All winter long the beavers can swim beneath the ice to this underwater pantry from the cellar entrance in their lodge. A fullgrown beaver requires the bark from a two-inch-thick tree every day; thus it must hide a considerable supply on the pond bottom before the water freezes over.

FAMILY LIFE OF MAMMALS

One of the important uses of the home, for mammals as for man, is to provide a safe place in which the young can be born and reared until they are ready to set out on new lives of their own. Many burrowing species are able to increase in number, sometimes to an alarming extent, because their way of living guarantees the survival of a great number of offspring to perpetuate their race. Since their young can stay hidden, it makes no difference that it takes a long time for them to mature. Baby prairie dogs, safely tucked away in their underground nursery, are not fully clothed in fur until they are three or four weeks old, and cannot see until five weeks of age. Many other rodents are born blind and naked; chipmunks and squirrels have no sight until they are a month old, and not until they are two months old can they be trusted to take care of themselves.

Fawns of the blacktail deer are difficult to distinguish in the light and shadow of the forest floor.

The young of the hoofed species which have no fixed home and which are constantly the prey of hungry carnivors are very precocious in their ability to take care of themselves. A buffalo calf can follow its mother a few hours after it is born. Fawns need only a few weeks of carefully hidden rest before they can move about with their parents. Such carnivors as foxes and mountain lions have young which are born furred, but they cannot see until about two weeks old.

In general, small mammals have bigger families than the larger species. This may be nature's way of offsetting the greater danger to the smaller species of being devoured by their big cousins. One baby at a time, which is the usual rule with human beings, is quite uncommon among mammals; the only species with a single baby in a family are the bighorn sheep, buffalo, elk, and the marine mammals. Among many of the hoofed mammals, although the mother may have only one baby for her first-born, successive litters usually include either twins or triplets. In the bats the number of babies is small, one or twins. Twins, and sometimes triplets, are born to the black bear, some tree squirrels, otter, jaguar, ocelot, and mountain lion. The smaller carnivors believe in larger families; raccoons have four to a litter, weasels and mink have five as have skunks and foxes, and coyotes have six or seven. The following common mammals are our most prolific: ground squirrels with litters of five to eight at a time; various species of mice and rats with litters of three to nine; and rabbits with litters of four or five. Not only are the individual litters large among the rodents, but some species have a dozen or more litters a year in contrast to the carnivors and hoofed mammals which usually have only one.

Wolf cubs could easily be mistaken for puppies.

A moose calf is an awkward animal with long gangling legs.

Mammals differ widely in the attention they give their young. As soon as the babies are able, they are weaned and taught to get their own food. At two months, the young woodchuck must leave the family circle; this time limit for a carefree childhood under the protection of the mother is about the same for young prairie dogs and tree squirrels. Neither mother nor father woodchuck takes any interest in educating the babies for the strenuous life which lies ahead. In fact they generally drive the young out of the home and force them to find a new territory in which to get food and build their own homes.

Among the carnivors, the mother rears the family and takes time to teach her babies some of the habits most useful to know. Father plays a very minor role indeed. When the mother black bear, for instance, leaves her den in March or April, she takes her two-month-old cubs and keeps them with her throughout the first summer and winter. She plays the part of teacher as well as mother with great patience. To do this, she generally has to forego having a family every second year. The mother raccoon also takes the time to teach her brood of babies how to find food, guard against enemies, and take care of themselves. Among the weasels both parents bring food to the babies after they are weaned, and during the first summer the entire family hunts together and plays together. Another happy family among the carnivors is that of the otter. The mother takes time to play with her young while teaching them the more serious activities of life; the mother introduces her babies to the water and teaches them how to swim. When she is sure the family is well on the way to becoming self-reliant, she allows the father to join them and he assists in the final education. A model family is that of the red fox. While mother has to stay in the den to nurse her babies, father brings fresh food to her. When the young are able to eat solid food, the father brings them meat also. Later both parents stay with the youngsters, teaching them the woodland lore they need to know in order to take care of themselves.

HOW MAMMALS SPEND THE WINTER

Mammals which live in temperate and arctic regions have to contend with winter living conditions which bring low temperatures and a scarcity of food. For most mammals, the low temperatures alone need be no problem, since they are equipped with fur coats and a warm-blooded condition to offset this factor. But for the herbivorous species, winter in the northern states means poor grazing when deep snows often cover the best available food; leafless trees and the few evergreens which are digestible are a poor substitute for juicy and nourishing grass. The carnivors are active most of the winter, with a few outstanding exceptions such as the black bear; but they must travel greater distances then to get a square meal since in winter prey is scarce. An almost universal urge is the hoarding of food. Nature seems to provide either a feast or a famine. When food is plentiful, a mammal will gorge until it can hold no more. Carnivors and many rodents will then hide what is left in a temporary cache. Among most of the rodents, thrift has reached such proportions that many species feverishly spend all late summer and autumn hoarding stores of seeds and nuts in their underground storerooms far in excess of what they will consume. A few species, as the woodchuck, lay up food reserves in the form of their own body fat.

Another solution to the problem of winter is migration. Birds have become very proficient at traveling south in winter, north in summer. But to avoid winter in this way means traveling thousands of miles, an easy feat for flying animals but a difficult one for pedestrians. For this reason few mammals have attempted to migrate. Some, like the elk, have summer and winter feeding grounds, but these are no farther apart than a few hundred miles. Migration is also the habit of the large aquatic mammals, but prompted by different reasons than those influencing the land mammals.

There is still another way for a mammal to evade the discomforts of winter. The energy required to carry on normal living activities comes from food, which is a fuel for the body "furnaces." Activity involves chemical and physical changes in the body cells known as metabolism; metabolism in turn involves fuel-consumption. Thus the more active an animal is, the higher its metabolic rate and the more food it needs. Many mammals seem instinctively to know this, and adapt themselves to a scarcity of fuel by banking their body furnaces—in other words by putting less demand on the metabolic machinery— and reducing their activities to a minimum. Thus in winter a gray squirrel or a chipmunk will feast until it can eat no more, retire to its bedroom and sleep for one, two, or even three weeks. While asleep its metabolic requirements are very low. When hungry, the animal wakes up, eats from its cache of nuts, and then takes it easy for another long period. The longest winter nap is taken by the bear, from late fall until spring.

A few mammals have learned how to suspend activities even more than in normal sleep. This is known as *hibernation,* a condition characterized by a lowering of the body temperature and a reduction of the heart beat and breathing rate. During hibernation a warm-blooded animal temporarily reverts to a more primitive cold-blooded state. It is a period of very low activity when the body furnaces almost go out, leaving only a pilot light burning; as a result, the demands on the fuel reserves of the body are incredibly slight.

In the biological definition of the term, a bear is not a hibernator, and many other mammals which spend months in a dormant condition are not true hibernators even though the term is sometimes applied to them. The bear's temperature remains high, it wakes up quickly and the female gives birth to her cubs while in deep sleep; the latter feat would be impossible for an animal in hibernation. Our real hibernators are the bat, woodchuck, ground squirrel, and the introduced hamster.

What brings about hibernation? Biologists have found some of the answers, but not all. It is agreed that one essential is a cold environment although low temperature alone does not always bring on hibernation. A hibernating mammal goes into this condition from a natural sleep, attempting to conserve what body warmth it may have by curling into a tight ball, with head tucked between the forepaws and close to its belly. The process of awakening takes several hours, and is not as simple as waking up from a nap. At first the animal makes feeble movements with its paws, and struggles and shivers; this raises the body temperature a little. The forepart of the animal becomes normal first, then the heart beat and breathing rate are speeded up. At the height of the awakening process the heart of a hamster beats 600 times a minute! Finally the brain takes over, consciousness returns, and the hibernator is able to carry on its usual activities. While these external signs of entering and leaving the hibernating state are evident, remarkable things have been happening inside the animal.

The constant temperature of a warm-blooded animal is brought about by a special part of the brain which acts as a thermostat. Like the thermostat in a home heating system, it regulates the amount of heat produced to offset that lost to the environment. So accurately does our biological thermostat work that the body temperature of a healthy person varies less than a few tenths of a degree. As we all know, our temperature as taken on a clinical thermometer actually is an index as to whether we are sick or well. In an active warm-blooded animal, as the environmental temperature goes down, this thermostat steps up the metabolic processes to increase body-heat production; in turn the body needs more fuel in the form of food. It is apparent that, during hibernation, the animal's thermostat must have been reset to permit a lower body temperature than normal. The body temperature of most hibernators drops from a normal of about 98°F. to a hibernating temperature of 40°F. to 50°F.; in some cases the rate of the heart beat is reduced from a normal 200 to 5 per minute. So effectively is the metabolic rate reduced that the hibernator's oxygen consumption may be only 7% of normal, and the metabolic rate itself 3% of normal. This means that while the animal hibernates, its food demands are reduced almost to the vanishing point. The philosophy of a hibernator evidently is, if you can't get food, do without it.

There is a limit to the cold that even a hibernating mammal can stand. The temperature of the burrow or den in which the animal is hibernating is usually between 40°F. and 50°F. When the temperature approaches the fatal freezing point, the thermostat goes into action and increases the metabolic rate, often to the point of awakening the animal. The brain does not carry on normal activities until its temperature is 68°F. or above; thus biologists believe that during hibernation the animal's brain is inactive and the animal itself is deaf. Nerves in the limbs can stand greater chilling but even they go out of business if subjected to temperatures below 36.5°F. In spring, as the thermostat again is set for normal warm-blooded control, the hibernator's blood flow and heart beat are brought to normal and the metabolic rates are returned to their more demanding levels. The awakened hibernator's first thought is usually of a hearty meal, to make fuel supplies available for its body furnaces.

We are not certain what stimulates the thermostat to bring about these changes. It is known, however, that it is this same thermostat which adjusts our body organs to stress, and which brings about normal sleep. When the biologist solves this mystery of hibernation he will probably also have the answer to why and how we go to sleep.

*

Everyone realizes that we are living in an era of tremendous advances in science and technology, and that the prospects for the future indicate even greater advances as man learns to harness new sources of energy. Much of this will benefit all mankind in reducing poverty, famine, sickness, and physical discomfort throughout the world. But at the same time science and technology are surrounding us with an artificial environment which is rapidly becoming very different from the natural one to which our bodies have become adapted by the slow process of evolution. One can change housing conditions, improve transportation, and even bring about social improvements in a few decades. But we cannot change our body structures and functions, our instinctive desires and satisfactions in such a short span of time, or as easily. Happiness in this man-made world will be more possible if we maintain some contact with the world of nature of which we are biologically a part. A harmonious relationship with the natural world makes us appreciate that there are some things which were created by a mind and spirit greater than those of man.

Realization of this fact is becoming more widespread. The trend toward suburban living, the desire for family vacations in the woods and at the seashore, the millions of new visitors to our national parks, the thousands of recruits to the ranks of amateur naturalists, the interest in programs and books on natural-history subjects, all seem to demonstrate the awakening of youth and adult alike to the need of keeping in touch with our natural environment.

Mammals are but one part of the wonderful natural world at our doorstep, in our backyard, and in our protected state and national parks. But they are a unique part of this world in one important way; biologically, mammals are the animals closest to us in their structure and activities, solving today life's problems in an environment similar to that in which our forefathers lived. A better understanding of our mammal neighbors can be the source of many satisfying experiences.

This book has opened your eyes, I hope, to the possibility of many hours of enjoyment in observing whatever mammals you may meet, in treating them with more sympathetic understanding, and perhaps even making friends of some of these ANIMALS IN FUR.

AFTERWORD

I am sure that you will not find the answers to all your questions about mammals in this book. Mammals are such an interesting group of animals that it would be impossible to put between the covers of one small book all the information that a young naturalist would desire. You will undoubtedly want to learn more about our animals in fur, and may even want to add a few more books on mammals to your nature library. Here is a list of some inexpensive yet valuable titles which I have in my own library, and which I have found very useful in answering my own questions about mammals.

A field guide is essential for identifying the species you will find in your nature explorations. *The Mammal Guide* by Ralph S. Palmer (Doubleday and Company, 1954) is the best of the recent books in this field. The author is state zoologist at the New York State Museum, and has brought together sufficient information, with color illustrations, to enable anyone to identify our common North American mammals. *The Field Book of North American Mammals* by H. E. Anthony, curator of mammals at the American Museum of Natural History, (G. P. Putnam's, 1928) is an older guide, and less adequately illustrated, but contains a wealth of information not found in other field guides. *A Field Guide to the Mammals* by W. H. Burt and R. P. Grossenheider (Houghton Mifflin Company, 1952) is a slim volume with a minimum of text and numerous color illustrations; an added feature is the group of photographs of mammal skulls which aids in identifying the skeletal material you might find.

If you wish to have one book which tells, in fascinating form, the story of the private lives of each of our common mammals, you should have in your library *Mammals of North America* by Victor H. Cahalane (The Macmillan Company, 1947). This noted mammalogist has compiled the biographies of outstanding mammal species of this country, and for each has written an exciting account of its life from birth to maturity. A college textbook in mammalogy, *American Mammals* by W. J. Hamilton, Jr. (McGraw-Hill Book Company, 1939), is the work of another distinguished mammalogist. Although a textbook, it contains much interesting information on mammal adaptations, migrations, distribution, behavior and homes, as well as on species which are particularly useful or harmful to man. A well-written book on one kind of mammal life, *Our Desert Neighbors* by the western naturalist E. C. Jaeger (Stanford University Press, 1950) includes short biographies of some of the most interesting desert animals. *Ways of Mammals in Fact and Fancy* by Clifford B. Moore (Ronald Press Company, 1953) is a collection of the many stories about mammals which are strongly entrenched in the belief of various localities in the country.

A few states are fortunate enough to have full-sized books published about their mammal populations. *The Mammals of Michigan* by W. H. Burt (University of Michigan Press), *The Mammals of Colorado* by E. R. Warren (University of Oklahoma Press), *The Mammals of Nevada* by E. R. Hall (University of California Press), *The Mammals of Washington* by W. W. Dalquest (University of Kansas), and *The Mammals of California* by L. G. Ingles (Stanford University Press) are a few such books.

A great deal of information on our American mammals has been published in various magazines. The *National Geographic Magazine* is a storehouse of information, with excellent photographs and color illustrations, on various mammal groups. *Natural History Magazine, Nature Magazine, Desert Magazine,* and numerous publications of zoos, museums and government agencies keep adding to our everyday knowledge about mammals, familiar or unusual. A more scientific publication, which however is understandable by the amateur, is the *Journal of Mammalogy,* official magazine of the American Society of Mammalogists.

Thus you will find that ANIMALS IN FUR is but an introduction to considerable amount of information on mammals, which is yours for the asking if you become acquainted with some of the above sources of dependable scientific material in a fascinating field of nature study.

INDEX

Every kind of mammal has a scientific name as well as a common one; the advantage of the scientific name is that there is only one for each kind of mammal, and it is used by all nationalities. We have discovered that many species are known by several names, depending upon the part of the country in which they are found. When you refer to a mammal by its scientific name you do not leave any room for doubt as to what particular animal you mean.

Each kind of mammal has a double name, indicating the genus and the species to which it belongs. The gray squirrel is called *Sciurus carolinensis,* with the name of the genus first and that of the species second, as if we said "Smith, William." The genus name *Sciurus* refers to the large tree squirrel group; the species name *carolinensis* refers to the particular kind of squirrel known as gray squirrel. A close relative of the gray squirrel is the fox squirrel. Its scientific name is *Sciurus niger,* with the same genus name as the gray squirrel, but its own species name. This would be like William Smith's cousin, "Smith, Robert." A still larger group of related animals is the family, which consists of a number of different genera (the plural of genus).

DIDELPHIIDAE. The Opossum Family

Opossum	*Didelphis marsupialis*	154

SORICIDAE. The Shrews

Smoky Shrew	*Sorex fumeus*	9
Dusky Shrew	*Sorex obscurus*	9
Short-tailed Shrew	*Microsorex brevicauda*	9

TALPIDAE. The Moles

Common Eastern Mole	*Scalopus aquaticus*	163
Star-nosed Mole	*Condylura cristata*	163
Western Mole	*Scapanus townsendii*	164
Hairy-tailed Mole	*Parascalops breweri*	163

VESPERTILIONIDAE. The Bats

Little Brown Bat	*Myotis lucifugus*	167
Pipistrelle	*Pipistrellus subflavus*	168
Big Brown Bat	*Eptesicus fuscus*	168
Red Bat	*Lasiurus borealis*	168
Mexican Free-tailed Bat	*Tadarida mexicana*	169

DASYPODIDAE. The Armadillos

Common Armadillo	*Dasypus novemcinctus*	157

OCHOTONIDAE. The Pikas

Pika, Cony	*Ochotona princeps*	62

LEPORIDAE. The Rabbits

White-tailed Jack Rabbit	*Lepus townsendii*	60
Varying Hare, Snowshoe Rabbit	*Lepus americanus*	58
Eastern Cottontail	*Sylvilagus floridanus*	56

Desert Cottontail	*Sylvilagus audubonii*	58
Swamp Rabbit	*Sylvilagus aquaticus*	58
Marsh Rabbit	*Sylvilagus palustris*	57

SCIURIDAE. The Squirrels and Chipmunks

Eastern Gray Squirrel	*Sciurus carolinensis*	25
Western Gray Squirrel	*Sciurus griseus*	26
Tassel-eared Squirrel	*Sciurus aberti*	26
Kaibab Squirrel	*Sciurus Kaibabensis*	26
Fox Squirrel	*Sciurus niger*	27
Arizona Gray Squirrel	*Sciurus arizonensis*	26
Red Squirrel	*Tamiasciurus hudsonicus*	26
Pine Squirrel	*Tamiasciurus fremonti*	27
Chickaree	*Microsciurus douglasii*	27
Northern Flying Squirrel	*Glaucomys sabrinus*	28
Southern Flying Squirrel	*Glaucomys volans*	28
Eastern Chipmunk	*Tamias striatus*	29
Western Chipmunk	*Eutamias minimus*	29
Columbian Ground Squirrel	*Citellus columbianus*	34
Striped Ground Squirrel	*Citellus tridecemlineatus*	31
Antelope Ground Squirrel	*Citellus harrisii*	32
Golden-mantled Ground Squirrel	*Citellus lateralis*	32
Prairie Dog	*Cynomys ludovicianus*	37
Woodchuck	*Marmota monax*	35
Yellow-bellied Marmot	*Marmota flaviventris*	34
Hoary Marmot	*Marmota caligata*	35

GEOMYIDAE. The Pocket Gophers

| Western Pocket Gopher | *Thomomys talpoides* | 39 |
| Eastern Pocket Gopher | *Geomys bursarius* | 39 |

HETEROMYIDAE. The Pocket Mice

| Plains Pocket Mouse | *Perognathus flavescens* | 46 |
| Kangaroo Rat | *Dipodomys merriami* | 50 |

CASTORIDAE. Beavers

| Common Beaver | *Castor canadensis* | 53 |

CRICETIDAE. Mice and Rats

Norway Rat, Brown Rat	*Rattus norvegicus*	41
House Mouse	*Mus musculus*	41
Muskrat	*Ondatra zibethicus*	51
Meadow Mouse, Vole, Field Mouse	*Microtus pennsylvanicus*	42

Eastern Harvest Mouse	*Reithrodontomys humilis*	44
Western Harvest Mouse	*Reithrodontomys megalotis*	44
Deer Mouse, White-footed Mouse	*Peromyscus leucopus*	44
Grasshopper Mouse	*Onychomys leucogaster*	45
Rice Rat	*Oryzomys palustris*	49
Cotton Rat	*Sigmodon hispidus*	48
Eastern Wood Rat	*Neotoma floridana*	47
Pack Rat	*Neotoma lepida*	48

ZAPODIDAE. Jumping Mice

Northern Jumping Mouse	*Zapus hudsonius*	46

ERETHIZONTIDAE. Porcupines.

Common Porcupine	*Erythizon dorsatum*	51

CANIDAE. Foxes, Wolves and Coyotes

Coyote	*Canis latrans*	117
Wolf	*Canis lupus*	120
Red Fox	*Vulpes fulva*	115
Kit Fox	*Vulpes velox*	117
Gray Fox	*Urocyon cinereoargenteus*	116

URSIDAE. Bears

Black Bear	*Euarctos americanus*	110
Grizzly Bear	*Ursus horribilis*	113

PROCYONIDAE. Raccoons

Common Raccoon	*Procyon lotor*	108

MUSTELIDAE. Weasels

Short-tailed Weasel	*Mustela erminea*	94
Least Weasel	*Mustela rixosa*	93
Long-tailed Weasel	*Mustela frenata*	94
Mink	*Mustela vison*	95
Marten	*Martes americana*	97
Fisher	*Martes pennanti*	98
Wolverine	*Gulo luscus*	100
Badger	*Taxidea taxus*	101
Otter	*Lutra canadensis*	103
Striped Skunk	*Mephitis mephitis*	105
Spotted Skunk	*Spilogale putorius*	105
Hog-nosed Skunk	*Conepatus leuconotus*	105

FELIDAE. Cats

Bobcat	*Lynx rufus*	122
Canada Lynx	*Lynx canadensis*	124
Cougar, Mountain Lion, Puma	*Felis concolor*	125
Jaguar	*Felis onca*	128
Ocelot	*Felis pardalis*	128

TAYASSUIDAE. Peccaries

Peccary, Javelina	*Peccari jajacu*	159

CERVIDAE. Deer

Whitetail Deer	*Odocoileus virginianus*	67
Mule Deer, Blacktail Deer	*Odocoileus hemionus*	71
Elk, Wapiti	*Cervus canadensis*	72
Moose	*Alces alces*	74

ANTILOCAPRIDAE. Pronghorn Antelopes

Pronghorn	*Antilocapra americana*	76

BOVIDAE. Cattle

Buffalo, Bison	*Bison bison*	78
Mountain Goat	*Oreamnos americanus*	85
Bighorn, Rocky Mountain Sheep	*Ovis canadensis*	82

OTARIIDAE. Eared Seals

California Sea Lion	*Zalophus californianus*	137
Northern Fur Seal	*Callorhinus ursinus*	138

PHOCIDAE. Hair Seals

Harbor Seal	*Phoca vitulina*	139

TRICHECHIDAE. Manatee

Manatee, Sea Cow	*Trichechus manatus*	149

DELPHINIDAE. Porpoises and Dolphins

Common Dolphin	*Delphinus delphis*	142
Bottle-nosed Dolphin	*Tursiops truncatus*	143
Harbor Porpoise	*Phocoena phocoena*	144

PHYSETERIDAE. Sperm Whale

Sperm Whale, Cachalot   *Physeter catodon*   145

BALAENOPTERIDAE. Finback Whales

Finback Whale   *Balaenoptera physalus*   146
Sulphur-bottom or Blue Whale   *Sibbaldus musculus*   146
Atlantic Right Whale   *Eubalaena glacialis*   148
Greenland Whale   *Balaena mysticetus*   148